The Mighty Thor

The Mighty Thor

MISSILE IN READINESS

by JULIAN HARTT

DUELL, SLOAN AND PEARCE

New York

First edition

Library of Congress Catalogue Card Number: 61-10390

MANUFACTURED IN THE UNITED STATES OF AMERICA

VAN REES PRESS • NEW YORK

TO AUDREY

whose patience and encouragement
contributed greatly

CONTENTS

ILLUSTRATIONS

following page 80

FOREWORD

The story of Thor is a story of achievement. It is also a story of people—dedicated people—in the military, in science and in industry, working together to fashion a new arm for the Free World's deterrent strength.

The story of Thor is short—as we measure time in major research and development programs. The first Thor contract was signed in December 1955. Less than three years later, an entire squadron, fifteen missiles with their associated equipment, had been deployed to the United Kingdom.

The story of Thor is a story of "firsts." First operational ballistic missile in the Free World. First missile to be launched from Vandenberg Air Force Base into the Pacific Missile Range. First missile to boost a payload into polar orbit. First long range missile in the Free World to record one hundred launchings.

The story of Thor is more—it is a story of space. Thor has earned the title of "Workhorse of the Space Age."

I am proud to be a part of the story of Thor.

—LIEUTENANT GENERAL B. A. SCHRIEVER, USAF
Commander
Air Research and Development Command

ACKNOWLEDGMENTS

Many of those to whom the author is indebted for their invaluable help appear by name in this book. Others we must mention here. All have our profound gratitude.

In the Air Force Ballistic Missile Division, there were Lieutenant Colonel Bill McGinty, Major Irv Neuwirth, and most especially Captain Tom Moore, who guided us through the labyrinth of Thor's complex genealogy.

In our work in England, we were helped by Lieutenant Colonel Jack Steffensen of Seventh Air Division, and Major Bob Spence of Third Air Force. On the Royal Air Force side, we are especially indebted to Tommy Cochrane, top civilian information officer at Air Ministry.

At the Pentagon, and wherever we traveled, our way was made smoother by Major Jim Sunderman, chief of the book section.

Industrially, we wish to thank all those at Douglas Aircraft Company from Dick Davis and Chuck Chappell through the ranks, but again most especially Larry Vitsky and Harry Calkins. Robert H. Jones of General Electric, and two other extremely capable men from Rocketdyne Division of North American Aviation, Dave Juenke and George Hall, contributed greatly.

There are just two more, Major General (British Army, retired) and Mrs. J. G. Denniston of Hythe, Kent, dear friends and gracious hosts who provided a deep feeling for the attitudes and aspirations of the British people, so deeply involved in this story.

JULIAN HARTT

ABBREVIATIONS USED

ABMA	Army Ballistic Missile Agency
AC Spark Plug	AC Spark Plug Division, General Motors Corporation
AEC	Atomic Energy Commission
AFB	Air Force Base
AFEX	Air Force Exchange
AFMTC	Air Force Missile Test Center
AMC	Air Matériel Command
AMR	Atlantic Missile Range
ARDC	Air Research and Development Command
ARPA	Advanced Research Projects Agency
BMC	Ballistic Missile Center
BMD	Ballistic Missile Division
Bomarc	An Air Force surface-to-air long-range guided missile
BOQs	Bachelor Officer Quarters
Caltech	California Institute of Technology
CEP	circular error probability
DAC	Douglas Aircraft Corporation
DEI	developmental engineering inspection
DFC	Distinguished Flying Cross
DOD	Department of Defense
DX	Highest national priority; a "crash" program
FRF	flight readiness firing
g	gravity
GE	General Electric
GSE	ground support equipment
ICBM	intercontinental ballistic missile
INS	International News Service
IOC	initial operational capacity
IRBM	intermediate-range ballistic missile
JATO	jet assisted take-off
LCO	launching control officer
lox	liquid oxygen
MATS	Military Air Transport Service
Midas	missile defense alarm system
MIPR	military interdepartmental procurement request

MSVD	Missile and Space Vehicle Department, General Electric
NAA	North American Aviation
NASA	National Aeronautics and Space Administration
NATO	North American Treaty Organization
OER	Officer's Efficiency Report
R & D	research and development
RAF	Royal Air Force
RIM	reception-inspection-maintenance
RP	rocket propellant
RSO	range safety officer
R-W	Ramo-Wooldridge Corporation
SAC	Strategic Air Command
Samos	Satellite and Missile Observation System
SM	strategic missile
STL	Space Technology Laboratories
T	exact instant of take-off
TAC	Tactical Air Command
TBM	tactical ballistic missile
TDY	temporary duty
Teapot Committee	Strategic Missiles Evaluation Committee
UDMH	Unsymmetrical dimethyl hydrazine
UOC	ultimate operational capability
USAF	United States Air Force
USNS	United States Navy Ship (an unarmed Naval vessel, contrasted to USS, etc.)
V-J Day	Victory-in-Japan Day
VIP	very important person
WDD	Western Development Division
WS	weapon system

The Mighty Thor

1.

PASTORAL, BY PLAN. . . .

England, 1960

THE winds of the world blew harshly in the late spring and early summer of 1960.

From Paris, the blasts of Nikita Khrushchev whipped through the halls of statesmen around the globe. His antagonism rasped from radios and television screens in the homes of ordinary people everywhere.

Never before had one chief of state publicly castigated another as Khrushchev did President Eisenhower. His attitude toward the entire family of free world nations was bellicose in the extreme. His position on the U-2 "spy plane" incident appeared utterly intransigent. By all historical precedent in the diplomatic intercourse between great powers, the Soviet stand seemed clear:

"Apologize, or else!"

But the United States did not apologize and, strangely enough, the anticipated "or else," the possible threat of armed conflict, did not follow.

3

Instead, Nikita Khrushchev retreated physically and figuratively behind the Iron Curtain. The fearsome world image of the Khrushchev of Paris—bullet-skulled, pyramid-bodied, like a baleful gargoyle atop the monolithic structure of Communism—suddenly shrank. It crinkled and deflated to the Khrushchev image of East Berlin, a noisome bully, petulantly blustering he would look into this again when there was a new American president.

His "ultimatum" of Paris was toothless.

Why? What stayed his hand?

Inescapably, one of the major factors stood in mighty array here in England, on the marshy fens of East Anglia, on the grain and pasture lands of the Midlands to the north.

On this jut of English coast, shouldering up from the Thames estuary into the North Sea, the free world's first completely battle-poised, strategic force of long-range, nuclear-warheaded ballistic missiles was ready.

The name of the white, sleekly tapering weapon was Thor.

It was no secret that the Thor could be launched in fifteen minutes, streak into space, then slam down on Moscow at ten thousand miles an hour, with a payload of almost indescribable destructive force.

Not even Khrushchev could have been ignorant of the significant fact that the last squadron, bringing a total of sixty "made in America" Thors to operational status, was commissioned between the Soviet "kill" of the U-2 and the abortive summit meeting.

At the moment of the summit, there were sixty new targets in England *he* would have to wipe out before he dared strike anywhere else. There were sixty new weapons, each with a preselected Russian target etched on its unjammable elec-

tronic brain, within certain reach of those Soviet targets, if he
did *not* wipe them out. . . .

And that is precisely why Thor was conceived more than
four years earlier: for this moment in history when it helped
tip the balance to the side of peace. That is why it was pushed
to completion and deployment under terms of secrecy and
urgency similar to the Manhattan Project that gave America
the atomic bomb.

Certainly, of course, no one could foresee, in late 1955,
the U-2 incident of early 1960. The first of those remarkable
high-altitude jet-sailplanes had not even taken off from
Lockheed Aircraft's plant at Burbank, California, on its initial
test flight.

Neither could anyone foresee specifically that Russia would
choose any particular incident in 1960 to reduce international
relations to their lowest, coldest ebb. Incidents come and go
with metronome-like regularity, and the import of one or
another cannot be guessed. The murderous Soviet suppres-
sion of the Hungarian revolt brought no war; a pistol shot
started World War I.

The key is whether a nation wants war, whether it feels
it has the margin of military power, which today we call
the "gap," to win a war.

In the 1954–55 period, however, the top levels of the United
States government, such as the National Security Council,
realized there would be a gap some five years ahead. Intelligence reports indicated Russia would have a dangerous
number of nuclear-warheaded ballistic missiles operational
by 1960. Engineering reports said we could not possibly have
a comparable number of InterContinental Ballistic Missiles
(ICBMs) to cancel out that threat.

The solution to erase the gap was the IRBM, the Intermediate-Range Ballistic Missile, to be based on allied soil, as an interim strategic missile. Its job: hold the line until our own ICBM forces—Atlas first, then Titan, next Minuteman—were operational in significant quantities.

They named it Thor, after the Norse god of thunder, traditionally a potent force in war but especially valuable in defense. Technically, the missile itself is the SM-75 (Strategic Missile 75) and the entire package is WS-115-A (Weapons System 115-A), including the support and launching facilities which make up the major part of the investment.

Behind those cold designations, however, lies one of the most exciting stories of modern times, in the individual, dedicated teamwork of people from American industry and the Air Force, people working in peacetime with a sense of urgency never exceeded in wartime, to put on the firing line in record time the most complicated weapons system ever completed.

Thor cost much.

Not only in money, but in effort, heartbreak, tears actually streaming down the faces of strong men, homes pushed to the breaking point, energy dissipated in the notorious Thor-Jupiter controversy.

There were periods of "cloak-and-dagger" operations necessary even in America, later in England.

There was need for diplomacy at the highest levels, to arrange launching sites on foreign soil despite Russia's "missile blackmail" policies, to work out careful arrangements whereby Royal Air Force troops would man the Thors, but United States Air Force troops would retain control of the warheads.

There was need for diplomacy at the lowest levels, with more than a thousand nomadic, gypsy-like American contractor personnel imposed on the countryside, the economy, the moral structure, if you like, of rural England, to the amazement of both.

And there were those who died, violently, in the service of Thor . . .

How well did it all work out; how worth while was the effort?

Lieutenant General Bernard A. Schriever, now chief of the USAF Air Research and Development Command, should know. He was the first commander of the ARDC's Ballistic Missile Division, which developed Thor, and later Atlas, to operational status.

After the collapse of the summit meeting, with no threat of conflict immediately resulting, General Schriever said:

"The fact that sixty Thors sitting there essentially can be salvoed [launched simultaneously at sixty different targets] should give [Khrushchev] pause for thought. . . . I feel this is a definite concern on the part of the Soviet Union. . . . I think the Thor presents a threat to the Soviet Union, and represents a sizable deterrent capability on the part of the United Kingdom."

Another check is to visit the station called "RAF Feltwell," the old grass-strip airdrome of World War II vintage. Here the first RAF squadron of fifteen Thors was turned over quietly to the United Kingdom a year before the critical summit meeting, and months before the fact was made public.

In the late spring of 1960 there were real winds blowing here, whipping the newly blossomed tulips bordering the parking area outside the neat, austere building of Feltwell's headquarters.

You notice them as the station commander, Group Captain Frank Andrew Willan, DFC, Bomber Command, one of the "end-user customers" of a program that started in Inglewood, California, a short four-plus years earlier, walks you out to his small British car for a tour of the squadron.

Already you've noticed that Andrew Willan kindles the same first-meeting impression as that of a benign but extremely watchful bear. In the light of international affairs and the responsibilities he carries both for the United Kingdom and the United States these are qualities to be admired.

Plainly, the Royal Air Force chose the personnel for Bomber Command's first ballistic missile force with the same care and precision that the United States Air Force used to guide the development of the Thor. Willan's top quality, for instance, appears to be patience, undoubtedly learned during nearly five years as a war prisoner after his Hampden bomber was shot down in 1940.

Another of Willan's qualities is a sense of history, which goes well with the quiet but obviously fierce attachment to the land he defends. Not far from here, you learn, is Colchester, site of one of the first Roman colonies in Britain. Your guide notes, too, the rich black soil of the swamplike ferns and remarks how wonderfully the celery grows there. But he also notes diffidently: "These really are rather new lands, reclaimed only in the middle of the last century."

But the future is perhaps most important of all to the forty-four-year-old, London-born officer, a student member of the Oxford University Air Squadron before World War II, and its commanding officer for a period afterward. Looking to the inevitable crises ahead, and the hope that this land and America both shall survive them in peace and in freedom, he must speak of another crop.

This is the Anglo-American planting of Thor missiles, rising celery-white from the billiard-table green and flatness of Feltwell, which Andrew Willan now tends.

They grow in clumps of three, these Thors, sharing certain common root systems drawing on common power supplies. Like each of the other squadrons—at Hemswell, Driffield, and North Luffenham—Group Captain Willan's has five such clumps, or complexes, for a total of fifteen missiles in the Feltwell command. These are discreetly scattered; no single enemy nuclear warhead could eliminate more than one complex.

As you drive through the countryside, you find some Thors lying somnolent under their retractable metal sheds, like sixty-five-foot-tall giants napping in the shade. Others stand erect on the sturdy boles of their eight-foot-wide metal trunks, getting their regular "exercise."

Resting or standing, all impress the observer with their silent aura of lightly leashed power, and the terrible potency of the incongruously small button-nosed packages at their tips, controlled by USAF officers at each site.

This potential is respected. As angry-horned bulls are carefully fenced, more to protect the rural populace than the bulls, the Thors are similarly corralled in their pastoral setting. Each launching complex is surrounded by man-high horizontal coils of barbed wire. Inside that is a ring of electrified chain-link fence. Outside are patrols of RAF troops and war dogs trained to be vicious. And through the night, the scene is whitewashed by floodlights.

What does Group Captain Willan think of this mighty weapon in his trust?

"It is altogether a wonderful weapon, an absolutely first-class weapon," he says thoughtfully. "It's rugged. It's well made. In five years' time, I think Thor won't be much in use. But I think it's now a most important weapon."

The proof of the wisdom in America's daring, admittedly risky decision to go ahead with Thor in 1955 scarcely could be stated more succinctly. There was the 1960 fact of a continuing peace, despite the most critical of times. The Thor was designed solely to fill that five-year gap from 1959 onward, to cling to the peace, until the ICBMs were ready in quantity to take over. Thor was doing its job.

Those physical winds sweeping down on the Midlands and East Anglia failed to snap the stems of the tulips. Hybridized to shorter stature for the specialized conditions under which they must live, they survived and bloomed.

The Thors, also hybridized from plans for the bigger but later Atlas ICBM, wavered not at all under the angry political gales from the Communist East.

Peace was the harvest.

2.

SCHOOL DAYS

Inglewood, California, 1954

IN the dog days of 1954, the people of Inglewood, a Midwest-flavored community surrounded by Los Angeles, had no thoughts at all about ballistic missiles. Their newspapers provided ample international excitement and crises in other directions. July 2, for instance, saw the armistice effected in the French Indo-China conflict. Little more than a month later, President Eisenhower pledged the United States Seventh Fleet would defend Formosa if the Red Chinese attacked. "Mr. K" was not yet in the language; most Inglewood citizens would have guessed that Mr. K was a horse running at nearby Hollywood Park racetrack.

Only a few shopkeepers on Manchester Boulevard, the busy east-west artery, took note of a new activity in their midst. It centered on the abandoned, deconsecrated parochial school, just one block from Inglewood's main intersection. At first a trickle then an increasing stream of briefcase-

11

carrying strangers began flowing in and out of the former schoolhouse.

Occasionally one of the "civilians" dropped in at the barbershop across the street for a haircut. Between the buzz of the clippers and the snip of the scissors, the barber would try an opening gambit: "I know what's going on over there . . ."

As the customer sat in silent, straight-faced amusement, guesses ranged from a new business to expansion of the Civil Aeronautics Administration, long quartered a couple miles west on Manchester near Los Angeles International Airport.

It was a fruitless effort. The barber might as well have brought up baseball in the first place. For this original group of "businessmen" actually was composed of United States Air Force officers, operating under strictest rules of secrecy. No more than a dozen strong at the start, under command of then Brigadier General Schriever, they were the nucleus of what one day would become the USAF Ballistic Missile Division. In five short years they would grow to an organization of nearly five thousand people, becoming the nerve center of the nation's long-range ballistic missile programs and many significant space ventures.

In the end, perhaps the barber had the last laugh.

This close little coterie of officers-in-mufti only *thought* they knew why they were there in the old schoolhouse. Like "Mr. K," the word "Thor" was not yet in their language, either. They firmly believed their sole reason for existence was to build, as rapidly as possible, a five-thousand-nautical-mile-range missile called Atlas, to carry a hydrogen bomb one-quarter the way around the world.

Perhaps no one starting in a new school, however, can possibly anticipate what he will learn there. Long before Atlas became an operational reality, these men helped to build the Thor ballistic rocket that would safeguard a later era's tenuous peace, carry America's first scientific package to deep space, and blaze the way for the exotic military satellites called Midas and Samos, tomorrow's successors to the U-2, which also played an unsuspectingly large role in the years ahead. They did not know they were going to build the "DC-3 of space. . . ."

One thing they did know: this assignment to Inglewood was the strangest domestic TDY (temporary duty) on record.

The Air Force, in common with the Army, Navy, and Marine Corps, is forced to enjoy an almost compound-like social status. In civilian life, plumbers, carpenters, lawyers, writers, chemists, and politicians, all may mingle freely at the clubs or taverns of their choice, for they carry in their minds no secrets affecting the future of their nation, perhaps of mankind itself. Most especially, they do not bear the burden of being on the public payroll yet unable to discuss with the public how they serve their purpose. The answer for the military is the Officers' Club, where people driven together at least can be together.

But in Inglewood?

There was no club within reasonable reach. And the top-secret nature of the job pushed those involved to extraordinary, sometimes amusing, extremes.

The officers, who changed from uniforms to civilian clothes aboard airplanes or in motels en route to Inglewood, and back again on leaving, quickly found themselves a handy officers' mess for lunch. It was the stand-up hamburger and hot-dog stand across the street, at the corner of Manchester and Hillcrest.

Recreational area? Easy! That was diagonally across the street, the big suburban Sears, Roebuck and Company shopping center. There a man could ponder quietly matters of thrust, gimballed engines, or inertial guidance, while browsing through the displays of salt-water tackle guaranteed to bring in "the big ones" from the ocean—so close in miles, so far away in available time.

Dances? Under the deliberately non-descriptive title of USAF Western Development Division (WDD)—the division created by a general order of the Air Research and Development Command (ARDC) on July 1, 1954, and later called Ballistic Missile Division (BMD)—one could rent the local Elks Club on an off night.

Wives' Club? There was nothing wrong with the Buggy Whip, a tavern in the nearby Westchester section of Los Angeles, on La Tijera Boulevard.

Coffee mess? That was the easiest. Just build a shelf over the sink in the old teachers' lounge in the schoolhouse, and plug the pot into the wall outlet. . . .

Despite these social amenities, this was not just an adult Western, a game of cops and robbers at the taxpayers' expense. This handful of Air Force people was picking up the cards in the most crucial game of "showdown" their nation ever had played. Whereas the atomic bomb *ended* a war somewhat earlier than could have been done otherwise, their assignment was to *prevent* another. They were under the strangest orders in history: build a series of weapons unlike anything built before, and of such potency we never will have to use them—weapons the very use of which could mean that the cause was already lost.

Thor was destined to be the first of that family. It constituted, by necessity, the greatest example of borrowing—and paying back—in all the technological history of weaponry. It borrowed people as well as ideas from the Atlas program. Then it paid back, through flights to test Atlas re-entry nose cones, before Atlas itself could fly. And it yielded bonuses along the way, boosting magnificently intricate payloads into space when national prestige needed them most.

But, to understand better the Thor story, let us look first at two elements: one, the personnel who in 1954 were assembling at the old schoolhouse in Inglewood, California, with the terrible knowledge that Russia would be able, in five short years, to destroy by ballistic missile almost every vestige of America as they knew it unless they could stave off that prospect by the product of their own hands and minds.

The other is the rather sad history of American missilery to that date, wherein the exhaust trails of rockets were only belatedly recognized as the handwriting on the sky, leading to the story of how we finally started in the mid-fifties, almost by accident, to meet the crisis of 1960.

3.

MAN WITH AN APPOINTMENT

En Route, Germany to
California, 1910–54

THERE was just one question when the day of the strategic, long-range ballistic missile dawned with tropic suddenness on the Pentagon in 1954.

The question: Who would direct the crash Air Force research and development program?

The instant answer: Bernard Adolph Schriever, just forty-three years old, brigadier general for barely a year, German by birth, American by naturalization, and Texan by osmosis.

If Bennie Schriever's shoulders seemed young for the vast responsibilities heaped suddenly upon them, with national survival intrinsically involved, they also were strong. With an already illustrious military career of more than twenty years behind him, he was ready for the challenge.

The unprecedented management-engineering problems seemed virtually insurmountable even to many of his superiors, but there was no hint of doubt in Schriever's eyes.

Behind them lay a top-notch engineering mind, trained as unerringly toward this moment as missiles toward their targets.

Bennie Schriever had not *asked* for creation of the job Air Force Chief of Staff General Thomas D. White called "a tremendous undertaking, surpassing even the Manhattan Project in scope and goals." Instead, he had *fought* for it, frequently at risk of incurring displeasure higher up. When he was assigned as Ballistic Missile Division commander, he was not given an appointment; he was keeping one.

Adaptability, resourcefulness, confidence, determination, physical fitness, and mental courage—all those factors which would be drawn upon so heavily—had been stored away steadily, inadvertently and otherwise, from the days of his childhood. . . .

Bennie Schriever was born September 14, 1910, at Bremen, Germany. When he was but six years old (and an early memory was of the Zeppelins throbbing overhead) the United States went to war with Germany. His father, a civilian engineer on a North German Lloyd Line ship, was interned in America. Mother Schriever packed up Bennie and a younger brother, Gerhard, now an Air Force colonel, and got them to America, rejoining their father as soon as possible. That was at New Braunfels, Texas, a German-American community. But the new start in the new land was ill-fated. Before Bennie was eight, his father was killed in an industrial accident in San Antonio.

One might expect here the start of a tragic story. Certainly the usual elements of adversity were present. But that would be without reckoning the qualities shared by the Schrievers, mother and sons. The mother buckled down to keeping them together and fed. The boys buckled down to becoming Americans and learning their lessons, as well as their English, Texas-style. Perhaps the real turning point was 1923.

That was the year Bennie Schriever became a United States citizen. It also was the year Mrs. Schriever took on a housekeeping job which included quarters adjacent to the twelfth green of the Brackenridge Park golf course, at San Antonio.

Aside from providing added family income through the sale of sandwiches and soft drinks to hungry and parched golfers, the location intrigued the future general into a study of golf as thorough as his later study of the missile game, when circumstances put him alongside the Pentagon "course" where that competition was played out eventually.

With a seriousness of purpose that stays with him still, Bennie Schriever accomplished three things against that background. For one, he became a below-par golfer in his teens. For another, he scored equally well in his mathematics courses, long before congressmen worried about how to interest children in such subjects. And at sixteen, a member of the National Honor Society, he was graduated from high school.

Times and circumstances affected his future once more. The place was College Station, Texas, and the date was 1931. Young Mr. B. A. Schriever was awarded his diploma by Texas A. & M., a Bachelor of Science degree in Architecture, and the United States Army gave him a Reserve appointment in the Field Artillery.

The times: early depression, definitely unfavorable to young men with shiny new engineering degrees, or even a yen for professional golf. The circumstances: Texas was the focal point of Army Air Corps flight training.

Hence, in July, 1932, Cadet Schriever began flight training at Randolph Field, eluded a statistical demise in the high mortality rate of accidents and washouts, and won his wings and commission as a second lieutenant in the Air Corps Reserve at Kelly Field a year later.

Assigned first as a bomber pilot to March Field in Southern California, Lieutenant Schriever moved on to Hamilton Field in the northern part of the state, then to Albrook Field, in the Panama Canal Zone. There he served a stint as aide to Brigadier General (now Lieutenant General, USAF, retired) George H. Brett, and first proved he would not be dazzled by stars when a course of action became obvious, proper, and inevitable. Lieutenant Schriever's goal: the hand of General Brett's daughter, Dora.

These were years of the doldrums for the Army Air Corps, however. Like many others, some of whom were destined to join him at Inglewood BMD headquarters many years later, Lieutenant Schriever went on inactive status in late 1937 to accept an airline job. He was flying the Seattle-Billings run on Northwest Airlines in January, 1938, when Dora Brett became his bride.

As the clouds gathered over Europe, Air Corps fliers soon started back to active duty. In late 1938, Schriever accepted a Regular Army appointment as second lieutenant, assigned to the Seventh Bomb Group back at Hamilton Field. But with his engineering-degree background, Lieutenant Schriever also was starting his move toward the missile age. Within a year he was a test pilot at Wright Field, Ohio. There he attended the Air Corps Engineering School, graduating in July,

1941. Just before the start of World War II, he was sent on to Stanford University for advanced studies. He had barely settled into the routine there when Pearl Harbor burst upon the nation.

With a sense of continuity fortunate for even more perilous decades ahead, the Air Corps left him in school, promoting him to Captain in April, 1942, and Major that June when he received his master's degree in mechanical (aeronautical) engineering. A month later, Major Schriever joined the Nineteenth Bomb Group in the Southwest Pacific.

He was Colonel Schriever by the end of 1943. In three years of the Pacific War, he flew sixty-three combat missions, participating in the Bismarck, North Solomon, Papua, Leyte, Luzon, South Philippines, and Ryukyus campaigns. By the last year of the conflict, he had become commander of the Advanced Headquarters, Far East Air Service Command.

There was no time for consideration of ballistic missiles in those busy years. For that matter, the Air Corps gave them no serious consideration either.

Valuable information *had* been available before World War II. It had been developed through a quarter century of devoted, painstaking, and brilliant work by Professor Robert H. Goddard, virtually America's lone pioneer in rocketry. The physics professor had proved that liquid-fueled rocket engines, with their own oxidants, would perform in vacuums comparable to space, where there is no air for other types of engines to "breathe" in combustion of their fuels. He had fired them to velocities faster than sound, had proved rocket guidance principles and that of multiple "stages." This knowledge he offered the government in the late 1930's.

The military services were not then interested. "The barrier to be overcome was not of sound, or heat, but of the mind, which is really the only type that man is ever confronted with anyway." That was the analysis later of Colonel Edward N. Hall, propulsion expert, one of the early self-styled "tong" members at the Inglewood schoolhouse, and first director of the Thor project.

Before Thor, however, Goddard's work was sought eagerly, for the Germans had "Goddards" of their own. As the Allied airmen began sweeping the Luftwaffe methodically from the skies in the later stages of World War II, the Nazis, of necessity, turned to rocketry as a substitute.

The result was the V-2, impossible to intercept as it reached speeds of 3,500 miles an hour, climbed to fifty miles' altitude, then plunged its one-ton pay load of explosives down upon England from two hundred miles away.

There were two fortunate aspects to the V-2, terrifying as its random, vengeful harvest of death and destruction was. It came too late to affect the outcome of the war; it came early enough to alert American military circles to a new recognition of the possibilities of missiles.

Once the shooting stopped, the race was on to snatch up a fascinating kind of booty none had anticipated a very short time before: the scientific booty of missiles, missilemen, and missile knowledge. Colonel Hall, for instance, led a group through German rocket plants and assisted in dividing captured equipment between Britain and the United States.

Many things of import to the future happened as that year of 1945 raced on through V-J Day, each with its bearing on the crises of 1960 and the threescore Thor missiles that then would be standing ready in England, armed with nuclear warheads. Three of the captured V-2 rocket engines, for instance, not in the best of condition but suitable for the purpose, were rushed for thorough evaluation to the North American Aviation plant alongside Los Angeles International Airport. Four years later, NAA formed its Rocketdyne Division, destined to receive the Atlas engine assignment, then to adapt the design almost overnight for Thor, virtually doubling the task when building the IRBM alongside the Atlas suddenly became a matter of highest national priority.

Two atomic bombs, at Hiroshima and Nagasaki, heralded a new age dawning in destructive capabilities, a new force for war that was to become a force for peace. Aboard the aircraft carrier U.S.S. *Shangri La,* after President Truman announced that the "new bomb" had the equivalent of twenty thousand tons of TNT, a Navy pilot kicked the tire of his F-6-F Hellcat, nodded at the five-hundred-pound bomb, and said, "I feel like a fool carrying that all the way to Tokyo!" He could not possibly guess that warheads of multi-million-ton equivalent lay ahead.

On October 31, less than three months after detonation of the only two atomic weapons ever used in anger, the Army Air Corps circularized a request to the nation's aircraft companies seeking ideas for missile development in the decade ahead. For the moment, it seemed that the United States was taking time by the forelock. But many factors dulled the edge of this initial impetus. They included high-level pride in traditional weaponry, political considerations, and shortage of two vital ingredients: money and know-how.

At the end of 1945, Colonel Bennie Schriever was home from the Pacific war for reassignment. With the beginning of 1946 he became Chief, Scientific Liaison Section, under the Deputy Chief of Staff for Matériel. It was the beginning of a three-year postgraduate course in the labyrinths of the Pentagon which does not, but should, lead to a Ph.D. in some still-unnamed discipline including everything from propaganda and diplomacy to current management and advance planning. In Schriever's case the substitute for the doctorate was the rank of General Officer, USAF, in the nuclear-space age.

Things began to happen at once, in any case. In the first month of 1946, the Army Air Force assessment of the German rocket program was in. It was decided that manned bombers would remain dominant in the decade ahead. Nuclear warheads, even the "Model T" types dropped on Japan, were so big and heavy it was deemed rocket delivery would be too expensive and impractical. There were too many problems still to be solved: how to achieve sufficient thrust to loft a heavy warhead into space on a ballistic, bullet-like trajectory; how to achieve acceptable accuracy on an intended target one-quarter the way around the world; how to shield the atomic pay load against the metal-searing heats anticipated when it plunged back into the atmosphere's sandlike, abrading sea of air molecules.

Two important items of missile rootstock were planted that year, however, destined to bear the fruit of Thor by grafting. One was the go-ahead to North American Aviation for research and development (R & D) on the Navajo missile project. This called for an air-breathing "cruise" type of jet-powered, unmanned vehicle acceptable to the aircraft-oriented thinking then predominant, but it was to be boosted initially by a true liquid-fueled rocket evolved from the V-2 studies. The Atlas and Thor engines a decade later were direct descendants.

The other was a contract to Consolidated-Vultee (now Convair) to proceed with Project MX-774, the first study toward a ballistic missile with the ultimate capability of a five-thousand-nautical-mile range. That was to become the Atlas missile, from which Thor was to be scaled down swiftly even before there was an Atlas.

It all became academic, however, a year later. In 1947, the Army Air Corps became the United States Air Force, but the missile budget was slashed from $29,000,000 to $13,000,000, and Project MX-774 was cancelled.

There were no public cries of dismay, for nearly all these moves were classified. The public was concerned with the problems of postwar economic adjustment. Convair quietly dug into its corporate pockets to keep Project MX-774 alive, even though long-range, surface-to-surface missilery was pushed back to fourth priority in the Air Force R & D schedule.

The shape of Pentagon thinking was evident in the following assignment of the higher priorities: (1) bomber-launched missiles, at both air and ground targets, (2) surface-to-surface missiles of less than two-hundred-mile range, (3) surface-to-air and fighter-launched air-to-air missiles. Clearly, the picture of future conflict was but a mirror of past conflict, with missiles merely extending the "gun" concept by a relatively small degree in the areas of defensive aircraft armament, artillery, anti-aircraft weaponry, and interceptor aircraft.

In 1948 and 1949 Convair conducted some flight tests with its experimental MX-774 vehicles. The sleek, finned rockets, thirty inches in diameter and slightly over thirty feet long, burned alcohol in liquid oxygen to develop some eight thousand pounds of total thrust. That was enough to send one hundred pounds to an altitude of 670,000 feet, and to prove some valuable points.

These included the gimballing of rocket engines for flight control. This, in essence, meant mounting them on a universal joint, so that the direction of the flaming exhaust, the thrust, could be swiveled in any direction. Hence, the missile itself would respond by veering in the opposite direction. Outside the atmosphere where there is no air to act upon rudders, elevators, or ailerons, yet where ballistic missiles would have to travel, this capability was vital for accuracy.

Another point that proved feasible was the separation of re-entry bodies, the nose cone that one day would contain the warhead. Thus the heavy fuel tankage and engine systems, constituting only a limiting factor upon distance and terminal accuracy, could be dropped off after they had boosted the warhead to space, imparted to it the necessary velocity of many thousands of miles an hour, and headed it carefully to hit the chosen target.

In a sense, this was a period of unconsciously squaring away, a lull before the intense activities and events soon to pile one upon another. Colonel Schriever, for instance, entered the National War College in August, 1949. Even the Air Force itself was preparing organizationally for unforeseen events, establishing the Air Research and Development Command to take responsibility for all Air Force R & D in 1950. This previously was the responsibility of the Air Matériel Command. The separation cleared the way for eventual establishment of the Ballistic Missile Division and the most streamlined weapon development system ever devised.

There was a new incentive for a reappraisal of the future, for Russia, in late 1949, detonated its first A-bomb. . . .

Colonel Schriever was graduated from the National War College in June, 1950, the same month Communist North Korean forces surged southward across the 38th parallel to launch that bloody, costly conflict. It had the effect, however, of quickening the pace and loosening the purse strings in other directions.

The Air Force, for one, turned serious attention again to the long-range ballistic missile as a means of delivering nuclear weapons. In effect, following the officially cancelled MX-774 program, the year-old ARDC inaugurated Project MX-1593, in January, 1951, which asked Convair to resolve a basic question: Should the intercontinental missile be ballistic- or glide-type? Should it follow the arching path of a bullet into space and back down to target, or should it merely be rocketed initially, then glide back down to the target on some sort of wing arrangement, making it slower but perhaps giving it more controllable accuracy?

The criteria demanded were tough, for atomic fission warheads of relatively small destructive radius were the only warheads that could then be considered. The boundaries were these: a range of 5,500 nautical miles (6,325 statute miles) and a CEP (circular error probability) at target of only 1,500 feet. That is, 1,500 feet was the maximum radius around the target by which the new weaponry could miss yet still destroy the target.

Convair plumped for the ballistic approach. The Air Force concurred. In September the code name Atlas was put on the project officially for the first time. But it still was not a crash program. The atomic warheads were big items, and the missiles to carry them would have to be monstrous affairs.

America's first hydrogen fusion device was detonated on November 1, 1952, in the Marshall Islands. This man-made fraction of the sun's power erased the island of Elugelab, leaving instead a trench beneath the Pacific's surface nearly two hundred feet deep and a mile long. Forces fifty times more powerful, more terrifying than the A-bombs were now at hand.

But not even this monumental blast particularly hurried the long-range missile program, and for good reason. The "device" at Elugelab was not a bomb. It weighed many tons more than any aircraft conceivably could carry. Missile delivery was out of the question, certainly, in view of the massive, complex refrigeration system required.

It was not surprising, then, that the USAF Scientific Advisory Board's *ad hoc* committee on Project Atlas, meeting a month later, recommended a continuation, but no speed-up, of the program. Under the chairmanship of Dr. Clark B. Millikan of the California Institute of Technology they proposed a step-by-step program of flight testing, first with a one-engine configuration, then two, then three, in a "one thing at a time" assault on the progressive problems of propulsion, guidance, and re-entry heating.

One person, however, already was setting small fires in strategic places. That was Colonel Schriever, now Assistant for Development Planning in the office of the Deputy Chief of Staff for Development.

He had long been sold on the future of ballistic missiles. Now the thermonuclear experiment in the Pacific added new zeal. That was a so-called "wet" device. Could a "dry" weapon be built, eliminating the cumbersome, complex refrigeration? How small could it be made? How light?

These questions, aimed at possible reduction in the size of the long-range missile and at relaxing its terribly stringent target accuracy requirement, in view of the hugely greater blast of a nuclear warhead, Colonel Schriever put to the nuclear weapons panel of the USAF Scientific Advisory Board.

That panel was headed by Professor John von Neumann, an outstanding mathematician, then of the Princeton Institute for Advanced Study, later to become an AEC commissioner, and destined to die before he saw full fruition of any of the weapon programs, such as Thor, that he was so instrumental in initiating.

Another member of the panel was Dr. Edward Teller, until mid-1960 director of the University of California's Livermore Laboratory and known as "father of the H-bomb." He already was pondering the matter of a "dry" weapon. Whatever answers Colonel Schriever might get, he could count on them to be authoritative.

Others also were asking important questions in the spring of 1953. One was Charles E. Wilson, Secretary of Defense in the new administration of President Dwight D. Eisenhower. He asked Air Force Secretary Harold Talbott to review all missile programs to date. Talbott turned the job over to Trevor Gardner, his assistant for research and development.

Gardner organized a special group, under chairmanship of Dr. von Neumann, to study the field of long-range ballistic missiles. It was called officially the Strategic Missiles Evaluation Committee, but became more commonly known as the "Teapot Committee." Other members were Professor Millikan; Professor Charles C. Lauritsen and Dr. Louis G. Dunn, also of the California Institute of Technology; Dr. Hendrik W. Bode, Bell Telephone Laboratories; Dr. Allen E. Puckett, Hughes Aircraft Company; Dr. George B. Kistiakowsky, Harvard University; Professor J. B. Wiesner, Massachusetts Institute of Technology; Lawrence A. Hyland, Bendix Aviation Corporation; Dr. Simon Ramo and Dr. Dean Wooldridge, founders of Ramo-Wooldridge Corporation.

The first of the wanted answers came in an alarming fashion, and from an alarming quarter. In August, 1953, Soviet Premier Georgi Malenkov announced the test of a hydrogen bomb. And scientific analysis of fallout samples proved it was "dry." At least it was proof that it could be done.

By October, however, Dr. von Neumann was able to report, in his role as chairman of the Scientific Advisory Board's nuclear weapons panel, the "thermonuclear breakthrough." The United States would be able to build thermonuclear weapons of small weights and sizes and of great yield in the megaton (one million tons of TNT equivalent) range.

The following month, the Teapot Committee began its studies of the strategic missiles program in light of the breakthrough making long-range missiles suddenly attractive.

Gardner also had been busy in other directions, for it was no secret in the Department of Defense that Secretary Wilson, the former auto builder, felt then that missiles traveling 6,325 miles in half an hour were a bit too exotic to consider. Gardner had armed himself, for instance, with a report from the RAND Corporation, the "think factory" at Santa Monica, California, attesting to the feasibility of such weapon systems, plus a report from Convair that it could convert to a crash basis.

Finally, with the findings of the Strategic Missiles Evaluation Committee in February, 1954, the many meandering freshets of effort, over so many years, came into dramatic confluence. The broad channel for a perilous future seemed suddenly clear.

Both the Teapot Committee findings and the RAND report strongly recommended that the Atlas program be adjusted to the new warhead development and speeded with higher priority and more money. They also agreed that an initial operational capability (IOC)—the first Atlases on launching pads, in the hands of troops, ready to be fired in anger, if need be—"could be achieved by the 1960–62 time period."

There was one major "if" to the prospect: this could be accomplished *only if* certain management recommendations were carried out, *only if* a new development-management structure was formed to centralize control of the entire program.

The professional reputations of those making the recommendations was such that they could not be ignored.

Results came rapidly. In March, Secretary Talbott authorized acceleration of the Atlas program. By May, thermonuclear tests during Operation Castle in the Pacific confirmed the von Neumann group's forecast that small, lightweight, high-yield warheads were feasible.

Highest Air Force priority then was assigned to the Atlas, and ARDC was ordered to "establish a military-technical group of highest competence" in line with the Teapot Committee report, and to pursue the long-range missile program "to the maximum extent permitted by technology."

The next step was the ARDC order establishing the Ballistic Missile Division (then called Western Development Division) at Inglewood, California, on July 1, 1954.

There had to be a commanding officer of unique talents to carry out the injunction "to exercise complete authority and control over all aspects" of the long-range missile, "including ground support, operational, logistic and personnel concepts, and all engineering decisions." And he was waiting in the wings: no longer a colonel, but now Brigadier General Bernard A. Schriever.

4.

TWO IN THE BUSH

*August, 1954, to
November, 1955*

THROUGH the last half of 1954 and most of 1955, the intermediate range ballistic missile (IRBM) lay like a strange, unidentified, extra egg in the nation's missile incubator. There were occasional stirrings, changes, and growth inside the opaque shell. But no one could quite guess what it was going to look like, or to what size it would grow. No one quite wanted to claim ownership without knowing how much feed it would require or get. Conversely, no one was quite willing to disclaim ownership entirely, for the same reasons. After all, the story of the ugly duckling had a happy ending.

General Schriever properly was much too busy setting up his own shop (referred to hereinafter as Ballistic Missile Division, or BMD, for the sake of continuity, even though it did not emerge officially as such until June 1, 1957) for the Atlas program to concentrate primarily on anything less than the specified 6,325-mile range and the ample problems that implied.

Like all previous efforts, however, each development seemingly aimed exclusively at the ICBM would have its fallout, in due time, for the Thor program. BMD planners kept all possible range requirements in mind.

One of the immediate requirements, for instance, was to hammer out a management structure with clear lines of authority and responsibility in order to prosecute effectively this staggering Atlas program. The Air Force Scientific Advisory Committee, actually an enlargement of the old Strategic Missiles Evaluation Committee and also headed by Dr. von Neumann, was charged with reviewing such management plans presented by General Schriever, Dr. Simon Ramo, and the Convair organization.

It was apparent immediately that neither the Air Force nor Convair had the necessary across-the-board capability to manage the entire Atlas weapon system in the role of prime contractor. The committee concluded that a single, impartial organization should be assigned this task of systems engineering and technical direction, to become, in fact, the civilian-technical "right arm" of BMD.

Universities and technical institutes were canvassed, but none was able to take on the job. Eventually, it came down to the Ramo-Wooldridge Corporation, which previously had been engaged in long-range analytical studies for the Air Force. Only with understandable reluctance did R-W take on the task, providing the organization eventually to be known (and referred to hereinafter) as Space Technology Laboratories (STL).

From the start, STL's technical objectivity had to be ensured by Air Force insistence it be excluded from the production of any hardware for the programs it would develop and approve. It had to maintain an arm's-distance relationship with all potential contractors for BMD so that its recommendations would carry no hint of favoritism. It was a tough position, but Dr. Louis G. Dunn, STL president, was able years later to remark, with perhaps rueful satisfaction, that "the rewards of our engineering are found in the production work of other companies."

One of the first of those rewards was the Thor.

Along still another line, General Schriever and upper echelons of the Air Force had another concern: to start as soon as possible a second, alternate ICBM program, a second string to America's ballistic missile bow. It would be patterned along different development routes, in case Atlas did not work out, to provide "greater assurance of successful accomplishment of the ICBM development mission within target dates desired."

Trevor Gardner came into this picture, as did the ultimate IRBM concept. Gardner, of course, knew that the Air Research and Development Command, with headquarters then at Baltimore, Maryland, was searching all avenues for a follow-on to the Martin Matador. The Matador, a guided missile of early vintage, actually was an unmanned jet aircraft boosted to flight speed at take-off by a solid propellant rocket.

As such, it was under the Tactical Air Command. Hence it followed quite naturally that any follow-on, even though it were a ballistic missile—following a bullet-path trajectory into space and back again, after burnout of the propellant, rather than a powered-throughout flight-path course, either programmed or radio controlled—still would be within the current concept of "tactical" ranges. One thousand miles was the figure mentioned as an optimum range in the so-called TBM (tactical ballistic missile) studies being invited in mid-1954.

With this and the need for a second ICBM program in mind, Gardner had an almost prophetic idea. In essence, it was this: "If we need medium-range ballistic missiles, this is what the British need as their 'intercontinental' ballistic missile [due to the United Kingdom's proximity to the Communist empire]. Let's investigate whether they can build their own, and if we can help them, then we won't have to bother."

The committee to review the guided-missile program in Great Britain was under the aegis of the Aircraft Industries Association, now renamed the Aerospace Industries Association, which represents the major airframe companies of the United States. It performed a friendly but hardheaded job, perhaps best epitomized by two of those who made up the committee membership.

One was Lieutenant Colonel (then Major) George R. Vanden Heuvel, who was directing the ARDC effort to initiate the TBM studies. The other was Elmer Wheaton, chief missiles engineer of Douglas Aircraft Company, later to become an engineering vice-president.

Both knew the business. Wheaton, a Pomona College graduate in physics, had joined Douglas twenty years before as a riveter on the DC-2 production line. He was high in the DAC research section when in 1941 it developed a guided bomb which could find its target with a television eye in its nose. He was the top Douglas man in the era of the highly successful Nike series. And he knew there was one tool necessary to swift development of missile systems. That was the electronic computer.

Wheaton searched diligently that fall of 1954, but he found just one suitable computer in England. "It belongs to a delicatessen chain," he reported. "They use it for inventories, and rent it out during its 'down' time."

Vanden Heuvel also brought a wealth of down-to-the-rivets knowledge to the survey. A Georgia Institute of Technology mechanical engineering graduate, he was an apprentice engineer at United States Steel's Homestead, Pennsylvania, works until one month after Pearl Harbor, going directly into aviation. By the war's end he had flown seventy-two combat missions in the P-51 Mustang, winning fighter-ace designation by destroying five and one-half German planes in the air and three more on the ground. His career veered in the missile direction immediately after the war, with assignment to Wright Field. For five years, both with AMC and ARDC, Vanden Heuvel was Drone Project and System Officer at Wright Field, providing unmanned aircraft for many purposes, including atomic tests, before going to ARDC headquarters.

With typical directness, Vanden Heuvel summed up the findings: "They would be three years behind us with our help, five years behind without it."

General Schriever certainly could concur with this pre-Christmas 1954 report. BMD that month had completed its basic configuration decision on the Atlas. Even with the small warheads, allowing great reduction in weight of the missile and a decrease from five to three engines, it still was clear that "the resources needed to do this are just tremendous." The United Kingdom simply did not have such resources.

Thus the United States entered 1955 with the knowledge that any alternate strategic missile capable of reaching Russia within the time limit involved would have to be an American product. If an early ballistic missile of tactical range were required, it also would have to be an American weapon.

On that basis, BMD began preliminary work on preparations for Titan as the alternate to Atlas. Simultaneously, Vanden Heuvel's project for the one-thousand-nautical-mile-range TBM was going forward in a routine, noncrash basis, guided from ARDC headquarters at Baltimore. Within weeks, the two programs collided head on.

General Schriever had invited Douglas Aircraft and Bell Telephone Laboratories, which had collaborated so excellently on the Nike program, to submit a team proposal on the Titan. Even though Douglas did submit a proposal on Titan, it was clear they were more interested in concentrating on the one-thousand-mile TBM being generated by ARDC. The conflict of interest was crystallized.

No time was wasted on letters. General Schriever was aboard his plane heading for Maryland as rapidly as possible. In a hastily arranged meeting with General Thomas S. Power, then ARDC commander, and the latter's staff, the BMD chief made his case: the ICBM programs held the highest Air Force priority, while the TBM did not. The shorter-range missile should not be in the position of denying such a respectable, and respected, segment of industry from the more urgent ICBM programs. General Power, later to take over the Strategic Air Command, proposed resolving the question by transferring the TBM program to the Ballistic Missile Division.

Vanden Heuvel, present at the showdown meeting, frankly did not like the idea. Atlas, no longer completely secret, was a glamorous program. He feared the transfer would be a death blow to the tactical weapon, that it would be over-shadowed and forgotten at BMD.

No one sensed more quickly than General Schriever that Vanden Heuvel "felt we had no interest" in the project to which he was so properly dedicated. The BMD commander then took the heat out of the argument with a suggested modification of General Power's original proposal. He agreed to accept the TBM project and pledged to give it whatever priority assigned by higher headquarters, but on condition Vanden Heuvel went along with the package to BMD.

This not only proved acceptable, but also helped clear BMD's decks to meet an increasingly critical situation which then was only beginning to crystallize in Intelligence circles. The Russians were shifting some of their programs, as well. . . .

General Schriever's growing team had enough problems of its own in the first months of 1955, however. It was racing to complete the first official Atlas development plan for the fully detailed, redirected, expanded, and accelerated program. The Strategic Missiles Evaluation Committee had specified in February, 1954, that this should be accomplished by the new BMD-STL management group "within one year."

Simultaneously proposals were coming in for the alternate Titan program. The von Neumann committee had recom-mended this to be a true two-stage rocket, with BMD-STL also assigned to determine whether an IRBM could be realized from the second stage.

And this, too, was the period when headquarters was being moved from the schoolhouse to the burgeoning complex of buildings being constructed on Arbor Vitae Street, just across the Inglewood city limits in Los Angeles. The construction and continuing housekeeping functions were the responsibility of STL, which also set up shop there, opposite the equally new Aviation Junior High School and a scant mile from Los Angeles International Airport.

Royal Air Force officers ultimately assigned on Thor liaison duty to "Inglewood," as it always would be called, reported officially that it would "be hard to find a more pleasant place to work" than this "most sensible location" with its ivy framed entranceways and walks. But the surroundings did not help BMD and STL find an IRBM in the Titan second stage.

In July, 1955, General Schriever flew back to Washington to brief the National Security Council on the ballistic missile programs. He had to report that the best possible missile that could be derived from the Titan second stage would have a range of only "on the order of eight hundred miles."

It now became a National Security Council request that the Air Force actively determine the best approach to achieve a 1,500-nautical-mile missile. This came as no surprise to the commander of BMD. The outwardly reserved, always soft-spoken general has a privately expressed philosophy: "We in this business should be able to outguess people outside the business." On that basis, weeks before, he had put a two-man team to work reviewing every known proposal made to date which might have a bearing on the final details of an entirely new weapon, which would be called Thor.

The motives of the National Security Council, of course, were not divulged. It meets in utmost secrecy with the President. It is privy to the latest, most authoritative Intelligence information on the capabilities and intentions of any potential enemy. And none of its transactions or discussions are ever made public.

But one highly placed source puts the situation of summer, 1955, in these terms: "This was about the time we realized we'd been snookered by those May Day fly-bys; that the swarms of planes over Red Square really were the same ones, flying out of sight, making big circles and coming back over again, while they really were concentrating on missiles."

Further, there was a committee headed by Dr. James R. Killian of the Massachusetts Institute of Technology, who was to serve as President Eisenhower's first personal scientific advisor in the post-Sputnik days. The committee's task had been to evaluate the true posture of the Soviet military establishment. Its answer reportedly was, in part, in the form of a warning: the Russians in 1955 had set new goals, increasing the range of their missiles from six-hundred-to-eight-hundred-mile maximums to a thousand-mile range.

The implication was obvious. Such missiles based in Russia would bring all of Europe and the United Kingdom under the direct threat of missile blackmail. This could be accomplished much sooner than American ICBM's possibly could be operational in sufficient numbers to constitute a stand-off deterrent. The free world structure of alliances would be imperiled.

In that light, the IRBM with a nuclear warhead, based on

friendly soil within range of strategic Russian targets, was no longer merely an attractive proposition, as it had seemed when the survey was made in England. It was becoming a necessity. . . .

National Security Council requests are not made idly. Neither are they fulfilled casually, even if they are anticipated to some extent. General Schriever had no reason to change or strengthen his IRBM review team. He already had the best available.

The BMD side of the house was represented by Commander Robert Truax, an outstanding Navy expert on loan to the Air Force. STL's member was Dr. Adolph K. Thiel, one of the top V-2 missilemen brought to America after World War II, who subsequently left the Army Ballistic Missile Agency to join Ramo-Wooldridge. Each drew as heavily as needed upon the talents of his respective organization. In the case of Truax, this included Vanden Heuvel at an early date. "Dolph" Thiel, from the beginning, had the able support of Dr. Ruben Mettler, STL executive vice-president, among others.

With the Atlas program moving into the hardware stage, and its major associate contractors for guidance systems, nose cones, and engines picked, the IRBM planners "had a pretty good fix on the state of the art in the various component fields." They also had guidelines in other directions. While having no information on ultimate deployment of the medium-range missile, for instance, it was obvious we did not intend to strike at Mexico or Canada, the only major nations within reach of an IRBM from the United States. Hence, it would be deployed overseas and this meant transportability. Since the feeling of urgency already was upon them from higher levels, they could deduce this meant *air* transportability. The dimensions of available cargo craft like the Douglas C-124 Globemaster, therefore, imposed specific size restrictions.

What Truax and Thiel had to work with, in essence, was a tinker-toy set of parameters from all the previous medium-range missile proposals, and from the actual Atlas program. ("Parameter" is a key word in the language of missiles, cropping up repeatedly in any discussion. Basically it is a mathematical term, meaning a quantity to which one assigns any desired arbitrary value, rather than a variable which can take on only those values made possible by the changing factors involved. In simplest form, it means determining all the specific equipment and arbitrary performance figures required—the parameters—then letting them "draw the picture of what the missile will look like," contrary to first drawing a sleek-looking missile, then finding out what can be packed into it, and what it will do.)

Propulsion was one parameter on which everyone was agreed. The IRBM rocket engine would be liquid-fueled, using "one-half an Atlas" booster engine, with 150,000 pounds of thrust, to be developed by Rocketdyne. Dolph Thiel, the brilliant, frequently excitable Viennese, could shrug calmly over that item. "Clearly," he said, "it is the only one available."

Guidance was a matter in which the Atlas concept was arbitrarily reversed. The big ICBM was depending primarily on *radio-inertial* guidance, requiring a ground station to transmit radio commands during the early portion of the flight, with an *all-inertial* system, entirely self-contained in the missile, as a secondary system to be incorporated in later models. The BMD-STL planners insisted on the jamproof, entirely automatic AC Spark Plug all-inertial system, sending the weapon to target on a fully predetermined course, as the primary system. The radio-command system became the backup system for Thor. This change-over in roles, with its ultimate payoff in the product, was proposed by Lieutenant (later Captain) John D. Dahien, who later left the Air Force to join the Massachusetts Institute of Technology.

Nose cone selection was an easier matter. "To be conservative," reasoned Rube Mettler, "let's use the Atlas nose cone being developed by General Electric." Designed for ICBM's much higher re-entry speed, it could undoubtedly withstand the lower temperature generated by the Thor.

Swiftly, the *possible* parameters were being winnowed down to a tight kit of *necessary* parameters. They, in turn, were sketching out the shape of the IRBM. Knowing the distance to be traveled and the weights to be carried, for instance, dictated the amount of RP-1 kerosene-type fuel needed and the amount of liquid oxygen required in which to burn it. These parameters spelled out volumes in cubic feet, and the dimensions of a C-124's cargo hold told in part how that volume would have to be taffy-pulled and patted into shape.

By late August, Truax and Thiel could declare that such an IRBM, if the Pentagon wanted it, would be eight feet in diameter, sixty-five feet long, travel 1,750 statute miles to target at speeds up to ten thousand miles an hour, and would have a gross take-off weight of fifty-five tons.

The question remained: Did they want it?

Their technical proposal was completed and first went to General Schriever in early September. He bought it promptly. A task force was organized to carry it on up through the chain of command. Heading the group bound for the East Coast was General Schriever's deputy, (then) Colonel Charles H. Terhune, Jr., mechanical engineering graduate from Purdue University with an advanced degree in aeronautical engineering from California Institute of Technology and a wealth of experience in missiles and nuclear weapons.

With him were Mettler, Thiel, and Truax. They made the required rounds from General Power at ARDC, to the Air Staff at the Pentagon, to Air Force Secretary Donald A. Quarles, recently appointed following the resignation of Harold Talbott. At the end of September, it had been laid before Defense Secretary Wilson.

"All we could do then," Rube Mettler chuckles in retrospect, "was go home, wait, and keep our fingers crossed." In that period, however, there were ample events to occupy their attention, both publicly and privately. During September, President Eisenhower and the National Security Council had assigned the highest R & D priority in the nation to the Atlas program, indicating to those with proper clearance that the urgency for missiles was growing. And on September 24, the day before the BMD-STL task force had briefed Secretary Quarles, President Eisenhower had suffered the serious heart attack in Colorado.

While this event left the public in a state of grave concern, if not actual alarm, there was turmoil behind the scenes of the pending IRBM missile decision as well. The House Committee on Government Operations was to describe it years later in these words: "The Joint Chiefs of Staff, excepting the Army member, recommended that the [IRBM] project be divided between the Air Force [for a land-based version] and the Navy [for a seagoing version] but the Army member strongly dissented and the Secretary of Defense decided to let all three services have a part in the IRBM program."

That decision, with its seeds of the Thor-Jupiter controversy and other ramifications then undreamed, was embodied in memorandums directed by Secretary Wilson to the secretaries of the three armed services, dated November 8, 1955.

One directed the Air Force to proceed with IRBM Number One, destined to be called Thor. Another directed the Army to proceed with alternate liquid-fueled IRBM Number Two, which would be known eventually as Jupiter. And the Army and Navy jointly were to develop a ship-launched version of IRBM Number Two. This never lived to be named, for the Navy withdrew in 1956 and launched the solid-propellant program leading to Polaris.

Such memorandums do not flash through the chain of command instantaneously. In fact, the order to proceed with Thor did not reach General Schriever at BMD officially until November 28. Oral alerts, however, do much to slash the red tape of paper work. By mid-November, Bennie Schriever already was rolling up his sleeves for the new task.

Terhune (later promoted to brigadier general and assigned as vice-commander of the new Command and Communications Development Division of ARDC at Boston in June, 1960) found a message waiting for him at his Santa Monica home one Sunday. "Please be home at 2 P.M. so General Schriever can telephone you," it read.

Promptly at two, the boss was on the telephone, breaking the news of the forthcoming Thor program. The words were guarded for security reasons, but none the less direct. The general told his Deputy for Ballistic Missiles, "There is the greatest urgency to get ahead . . . on as compressed a time scale as we can get."

Terhune, one of the first five officers assigned to the schoolhouse, was instructed to prepare for a pre-proposal briefing of potential prime contractors for the major task—airframe construction, assembly, and testing—"within a few days."

Secretary Wilson's directives had placed two birds in the bush. Bennie Schriever wanted his in hand first.

5.

CHRISTMAS SHOPPING

Building Three
November 28 to December 23, 1955

THE teletype message from the Pentagon concerning "IRBM Number One" clattered into the message center of Building Three in the BMD-STL complex at Inglewood on November 28. It said, "Program approved, proceed at maximum pace." Colonel Terhune was ready for it. The moment the official flimsy was in his hand, he placed three swift, long-planned telephone calls. One after another, he talked to the responsible people at each of three great airframe companies. These were the firms preselected to bid on the prime contract for Thor's "airframe, assembly, and testing." They had been chosen on their proven ability to handle large emergency fabrication and management problems. Terhune asked them to send their top executives and engineers for a briefing on what had to be done in a new, similar situation.

And he set the pace that was to follow in scheduling the briefing for November 30, just two days away.

Sitting as chairman that day, Colonel Terhune laid it on the line. The Air Force was inviting them to bid on a missile of a range and type none of the three, or anyone in the free world, ever had built before. Moreover, they would have to put it on the firing line more speedily than anything of comparable scope they had produced before.

The round-faced officer, with the same "younger-than-his-years" look as General Schriever, sitting nearby, started with a background of the IRBM program, the technical design features, the fact that they "would use ICBM components wherever possible." He made clear that the Air Force was not so much interested in receiving from them proposals on *what* they would build—that already was decided in general by BMD-STL—but proposals as to *how* they would handle the job from a management standpoint. Then he came to the crux of the matter. He told them it was to be "a maximum risk program." Chances should, and would, be taken to insure early results "under the same ground rules as the ICBM program, and with equal priority."

"Probably in weeks," Terhune told them, "we will arrive at a final configuration and move forward, of necessity, without restudies. . . . The first design you fly should be the fundamental design you end up with . . . We want, as an early product of this program, a demonstrated 1,500-nautical-mile flight."

The attentive gathering of airframe engineers and executives realized at once there would be no prototypes for testing before production lines were set up, no typical aircraft-type development program.

Terhune, expertly building his introduction to a climax, topped it off by announcing the IOC date, when the first weapons had to be operational with trained troops at combat launching sites. It was January, 1960, just four years hence. That, literally, was a shocker. The average development cycle from idea to operational weapon system, such as a big bomber, traditionally was seven years!

Louis Dunn, STL's chief, and Rube Mettler took over the meeting to sketch a more detailed technical picture of Thor. A more skillful pair scarcely could have been chosen. Both had earned their engineering degrees from bachelors and masters through doctorates at the California Institute of Technology. Dunn, dark-eyed with a heavy, straight-back thatch of graying hair, had come to this task from the directorship of Caltech's Jet Propulsion Laboratory which was eventually to become the National Aeronautics and Space Administration's spacecraft laboratory. While at Caltech he was awarded the Presidential Medal of Merit for his World War II work on torpedoes. The younger Mettler, his high hairline already slipping higher to leave a close-cropped dark forelock almost alone, but with a ready humor to remind one of his youthful bounce and energy, had his own wealth of honors. Just the previous year, in 1954, he had received the coveted Eta Kappa Nu award as the nation's most outstanding young electrical engineer.

Together they explained the essence of the program: "There would be no time to make mistakes."

Dunn and Mettler promised that a Rocketdyne engine model of the final shape and size, with the final plumbing connections of concern to the airframe builder, would be available in March, approximately three months after the briefing. Around this model a mock-up of the missile could be built.

Research and development versions of the rocket engines would be roaring in tied-down static tests in the Santa Susana Mountains, at the far end of San Fernando Valley, by June. "Deliveries of production engines," the STL men warned, "will start two months after that." Warning was the proper word. It meant whichever firm won the contract would have to freeze the design of the missile, tall as a six-story building, reduce it to working blueprints, set up a production line, and have the gleaming monsters rolling off the end of that line in little more than six months.

The same winning firm also would be responsible for assembly of the Thor's complex components into the missile structure, and for testing of the total weapon. To give them a feel for these phases, Dunn and Mettler went into the guidance system, the warhead weight, and the nose-cone design, all to be adapted from the Atlas system.

Above all, however, the briefing team laid most emphasis on the fact that they were not calling for breakthroughs. Their program was based on the current state of the art, on presently known skills, abilities, and techniques. The new departure they were calling for was a management team that could pull these together in the most efficient manner and perform a major task in unprecedented time. This was carrying out Bennie Schriever's basic insistence upon top-level company support in keeping with the government-assigned priority.

At the end of the briefing, the representatives of the competing firms trooped out of Building Three with another stringent injunction ringing in their ears:

"Be back in a week, on December 8, with your proposals."

Neither the world in general nor the little group at BMD-STL in Inglewood were waiting particularly for the three companies to work out their proposals that week. The average citizen, totally ignorant of Thor and its ultimate role in England, was more likely touched by Princess Margaret's recent poignant announcement, "I would like it to be known that I have decided not to marry Group Captain Peter Townsend." A few, perhaps, were concerned over the developing situation in the Middle East, where Egypt's Nasser was bartering for arms from Communist Czechoslovakia, and where Israel's appeal to the West for arms was turned down by President Eisenhower and Prime Minister Anthony Eden. It is extremely doubtful, however, whether Dunn and Mettler were even aware of these developments. Once the briefing was concluded,they took off by plane like scalded salesmen to the AC Spark Plug Division of General Motors at Milwaukee and the General Electric Missile and Space Vehicle Department (as it finally was titled) at Schenectady. The trip was for a good reason.

While they had spoken confidently of the on-time availability of the AC guidance and GE nose-cone subsystems, they had to check on the instant outlook of each now that the massive program was beginning to roll. The truth was that GE's nose cone actually existed only in a wooden model, and that the Atlas organization had rejected the possibility that all-inertial guidance would be ready for operational missiles in 1960.

On the prompt arrival of each part, of each component of each subsystem, fully tested in turn up the ladder of growing complexity, on the specific date planned, depended the success or failure of the entire concept of *concurrency* upon which the ballistic missile program was based. Concurrency went much further than the construction of the first missile on schedule, however. It meant overlapping research and development, production, launching facilities, troop training, and the build-up of the IOC force from one initial launching site to the full complement of the UOC, or ultimate operational capability, with the first operational units expected to feed back experience to a still continuing R & D program.

This was a distinct change from the classic pattern of an aircraft program, in which prototypes are test-flown repeatedly and virtually all R & D is completed before a production capability is established. Only then is an initial operational capability feasible, and by then years have gone by.

"This is a long time," General Schriever has observed in explaining the concept of concurrency, "especially in view of limited in-service life and rapid technological advances which today quickly outmode many weapons systems."

The solution was to telescope many of the phases previously done "in series . . . to shorten the development cycle by taking concurrent development, production, and operational actions."

Such a dramatic concept, borrowing in part from the Manhattan Project and rivaling it in necessity and size, obviously entailed risk. General Schriever cites two reasons for taking risks of such magnitude. They are "promise of success and great potential." Thor possessed both. It had the promise of success because of the painstaking studies at BMD-STL based upon experience to date with Atlas. It had the most valuable of potentials, that of keeping the peace. The realization of both took another step forward with the submission of the three management proposals on December 8, 1955.

On the shoulders of eleven officers and civilians then fell the solemn, vastly responsible duty of deciding which of the three should be chosen to manage the Thor program. In Air Force terms, they constituted the Source Selection Board. To save time, deemed the most precious element in the program, General Schriever reconvened the same board which had served in selecting the prime contractor for the Titan alternate ICBM. There was but one exception. Lieutenant Colonel Vanden Heuvel replaced the previous recorder.

Colonel Terhune was president. The others were Colonel Lawrence D. Ely, since retired and now with STL; Lieutenant Colonel Joseph D. Heck, Jr.; Major Prentice D. Peabody, now lieutenant colonel and executive officer of the 6555th Missile Test Wing at Patrick AFB; Major James E. Early; Captain Arthur O. Bovier, Jr., now major; and four civilian experts, Charles E. Richardson, S. W. Dunham, Roy A. Watkins, and Raymond S. Blocker.

In strictest secrecy and almost around the clock, each made his individual estimate of each company concerned, in relation to an extremely exacting, carefully weighted series of questions.

This procedure is not in any sense an over-all evaluation

of any company, but an analysis of its relative merits in relation to a given project at a given moment. The points judged ranged from availability of facilities, tools, skilled and unskilled manpower, engineers, management personnel, and whether separate chains of command would be established for the specific project, to what effect the award of the program to each particular firm would have upon the performance of other important projects.

In the end, one firm was recommended. Each member of the board signed all copies of the report. Colonel Terhune then took it to General Schriever.

The commander of BMD quickly reviewed it, approved it, and sent Terhune winging East for the further approvals needed at other and higher levels. In only two days, Terhune "ran it past," almost literally, Air Matériel Command at Dayton, Ohio; Air Research and Development Command at Baltimore; the Air Staff at the Pentagon, and the Air Force Secretary.

Normal time for determining a prime contractor, from industry proposals to notification of the winner, was six to eight weeks. On the Thor program, it was completed in less than three. By the evening of December 23, BMD at Inglewood was authorized to address a telegram to the aircrafter's top officer, asking that those empowered to sign contracts "present themselves, with corporate seal," at the earliest date.

6.

HOLIDAY SURPRISE

December 24, 1955, to January 1, 1956

THE telegram was delivered to a home in the quiet, euca-
lyptus and pepper tree shaded community of Rolling Hills,
on the cliff-sided peninsula that forms the southern reach of
Santa Monica Bay and the western rim of Los Angeles Harbor. It was the residence of Donald Douglas, Sr., whose
Douglas Aircraft Company had given the nation the DC-3
"work horse of the airways." Now he was called upon to
provide a different kind of vehicle to deter war, and one
which would become known as the "work horse DC-3 of
space." In his role as chairman of the board, he quickly
passed the word to his son, Donald Douglas, Jr., president
of Douglas Aircraft Company. Well aware of the urgency, he
did not stop there, even though it was the day before Christmas. The missile engineering staff had to be alerted at once.
From long tradition he knew where to find them at this noon-
time hour of this most particular day. . . .

The Fox and Hounds, on Wilshire Boulevard in Santa

Monica, a mile or so from the Palisades and the sea, is one of those restaurants peculiar to Southern California. It blends the happy mood of an English tavern, the quiet, efficient hospitality of the South, the leathered comfort of a club, and a cuisine catering with equal aplomb to the diet of ulcered executives, the cultured tastes of gourmets, or the calorie-rich demands of the expense-account crowd. Representatives of all can be found during any luncheon period, watching or not, as their individual moods dictate, one of the frequent shows displaying California fashions on mannequins even more attractive than their sisters in films. Except on this particular day.

The decorations had done their best to create a Christmas spirit in a land where snow was only something to put on mountaintops for skiers. Scotch-and-sodas and martinis were doing their best, too, to replace the Tom and Jerries that were too warm, too rich for a sun-soaked, grass-growing December. But the groups were the same company-family types found anywhere on the day before Christmas. The almost equally divided male and female group in the alcove at the rear, with the big round table, was typical.

These were Douglas Aircraft Company engineers, keeping up the pleasant custom of knocking off work early on Christmas Eve. The men included Elmer Wheaton, R. L. Johnson, Chuck Perry, Max Hunter, Jack Bromberg, Hal Thomas, and several others.

A waiter threaded his way to the table and leaned close to Wheaton. "Mr. Douglas, senior, is on the telephone," he said, but not quite low enough for no others to hear. Wheaton, a blue-eyed fellow of massive brow that gives one the impression of a much bigger physique than he really has, excused himself. No one sang "Jingle Bells." The tempo of the conversation dropped. Everyone was waiting. Someone spoke up, "Oh, boy! I'll bet I know what that is!"

Minutes later, Wheaton came back. No one had to ask the answer. There was a grin splashed all the way across his face. Everyone had another drink, almost before he could get the words out, "We've been selected!"

When the opportunity came, Wheaton slipped beside Jack Bromberg and told him privately, "You've got a new job." Bromberg knew what that meant. He was to be Thor program chief. At the moment, he was not entirely sure that was good. After years of the Army Nike program, developing the anti-aircraft guided missile from the powder-and-ball Ajax days to the era of the atomic-warheaded Hercules, able to destroy a fleet of enemy planes instead of just one, he had been happy to find it settling down to a home-at-night routine. But, still, here was a new challenge. . . .

The news, for the instant, made the party even gayer than anticipated. It also made it shorter. The engineers knew there was work to be done that afternoon, Christmas Eve or not. The Air Force wanted the contract signed as fast as possible. There were work statements and other documents to be started, which would be needed in the first meetings with BMD-STL.

The Douglas team knew what had to be done. Elmer Wheaton had been in charge of all Douglas missile programs for a decade. Jack Bromberg, designer and builder of racing planes before he joined Douglas in 1934, had been pushing the Nike program for an equal period, with the energy-packed walk-fast native Chicago attitude that his transplanting to California had failed to eliminate. Hal Thomas, involved with missiles for five years and due to become Bromberg's assistant on the Thor, also was a Nike veteran. They and other Douglas engineers had worked together on the original TBM proposals.

All had participated in the Douglas-funded studies, which were begun in 1953 and cost "well over one million dollars in company funds," in order to take a look into the future of missiles and be ready for the day of truly long-range ballistic weapons. That resulted in a team effort with Bell Telephone Laboratories, for guidance, to win the Titan program. It did not succeed, but it was important because of their proposal of a solid-fueled ICBM as an alternate. The latter idea they took to the Navy. It appeared certain Douglas was in line for a predevelopment study contract of a Polaris-type concept when the November 8, 1955, memorandums assigned the seagoing service to liquid-fueled IRBM Number Two as a joint effort with the Army. By the time the Navy withdrew in favor of Polaris, Douglas was too busy with Thor to participate. The best the Santa Monica team could do years later was to remark with understandable pride, as Wheaton did, that "a lot of admirals still give us credit for getting the Navy interested in it."

In any case, their holiday work set the wheels in motion to get the Santa Monica plant ready for the job ahead, in terms of personnel, tools, and space.

Meanwhile, the necessary contract was being prepared in Inglewood, a dozen miles away across a corner of western Los Angeles. It was a letter contract, simply rewritten swiftly from the Atlas contract, purposely vague in many areas because the product was not yet defined, filled with many pages of what is termed "boiler plate." Its chief purpose was to get the job under way. Niceties could be ironed out later.

The papers, the Air Force, and Douglas were ready by December 28. Donald Douglas, Jr., climbed in his car and drove to BMD's Building Three to put his signature on the documents, bringing with him the other needed officers "with corporate seal." In the face of the implied emergency, the company had waived the usual time-consuming routine of processing everything through its legal department.

From the Air Force side, it had been equally a matter of good faith. Young Douglas arrived to find the contract ready for signing by himself for the firm and by Lieutenant Colonel W. D. Smith for Air Matériel Command, the hardware buying arm. On the strength of the grapevine alert, Colonel Terhune had sent a memo days before that to Colonel Harold Morris, chief of the special AMC office in Inglewood, to start preparing the papers in the interests of conserving every day possible.

Obviously, by the first day of 1956, BMD-STL and their new prime contractor had reached mutual understanding that Thor-in-being at the earliest possible date was above and beyond routine business. None could guess the hurdles and hazards ahead, the frustrating combinations of delays and shortened schedules resulting from political complications, both domestic and foreign, as well as technical problems. For the moment, it seemed Thor was off to a running start. All attention was focused on a critical step from which there could be no returning at a later date.

That was the "sizing of the missile."

7.

TAILORING TO SIZE

Santa Monica, California
January, 1956

THERE are many tricks to sizing a missile. Most are mathematical. Some can be psychological. Both approaches were employed in the first half of January as the Thor IRBM began to take shape on the blackboards and scratch pads of Douglas engineers, with BMD-STL representatives peering over their shoulders. The psychology, however, was all on the BMD-STL side and was employed chiefly at the suggestion of Rube Mettler.

The IRBM studies concluded the previous August actually had sized the Thor right down to its total weight of 110,000 pounds. It would have been simple enough to turn all this work over to Douglas and say, "This is what we want; start building." Mettler counseled that this would be too much like "shoving it down their throat." He proposed that it was far better to hand Douglas the now specific parameters and let them work out the general sizing and configuration.

This procedure had a double motive. First, it would provide an independent check on the previous findings of the Truax-Thiel studies. Perhaps even more important, it would give Douglas the incentive of meeting Douglas-set goals in the product. The obligation to succeed inevitably would be stronger if the contractor had no grounds to come back with a 1,300-, instead of a 1,500-nautical-mile missile, and say, "Well, you told us to build it this way."

Not that anyone anticipated such a result. There was just too much at stake, in the expenditure of money and effort, in the future safety of the nation and its free world allies, to overlook any bets toward insuring the still unproven concept of concurrency. Douglas Aircraft would be tooling up and, in the parlance of the missile business, be "bending tin" in a few weeks. AC Spark Plug would be constructing a new plant. Rocketdyne would be forced to establish facilities at Neosho, Missouri, for engine production. General Electric was destined to transplant its nose-cone operations to Philadelphia. Against all this, Rube Mettler wanted as much "money in the bank" as possible. He explained why in layman's language: "Concurrency is wonderful if you're right. It's awful if you're wrong. If something really goes wrong, we could really look sick."

Jack Bromberg, the Douglas project director, Hal Thomas, his assistant, and the swiftly growing engineering team completed their work by January 15. Dolph Thiel, who for all practical purposes had moved to the Santa Monica plant in that period, was understandably elated at the sizing results.

It came out within 1 per cent of the 110,000-pound weight of the earlier BMD-STL studies. There was but one basic change in configuration of the missile. The BMD-STL technical proposal had foreseen a cylindrical booster shape. Douglas called for a tapering, slightly conical shape. The Air Force bought it. It did give a slightly better aerodynamic shape. There also was a fabrication difference on the rigid tankage for the RP-1 kerosene-type fuel and the liquid-oxygen (lox) oxidant. STL preferred all-welded tanks, while Douglas proposed a method of securing bulkheads with bolts. Tests proved the Douglas system was adequate, and it also was accepted.

This swift and happy meeting of minds held a private bonus for Rube Mettler, STL's Thor project director. The satisfactory sizing and shaping of Thor on the parameters given Douglas left the program with a one-thousand-pound "bank account," a margin for error quietly built into the specifications.

Their best judgment said that the thrust variation of the Rocketdyne rocket engine would be "plus or minus 1 or 2 per cent." They told Douglas it might be "plus or minus 7 per cent."

The guidance system needed engines that could be gimballed three to four degrees, swinging the exhaust nozzles that much to put Thor on course and keep it there. Douglas was told nine degrees.

Mettler unblinkingly introduced these "wide design margins to keep a technical reserve for contingencies." He could back it up with a solid argument: "We know this is a crash program, with no time to make mistakes. We want a position where we don't have to demand perfection, where it is reasonable to proceed concurrently, and to say: 'Build on production tooling from the beginning and, in view of the state of the art and the margins, it'll go the 1,500 miles.'"

Inherent in that, of course, was the corollary that the payload also would be delivered within the now required two-mile CEP.

The go-ahead for production tooling-up, to start designing and spotting the jigs and fixtures at Santa Monica, came shortly afterward at a meeting of Dunn, Mettler, Thiel, Bromberg, Johnson, and BMD's representatives. Colonel Harold Norton, assistant deputy chief for technical operations, who had guidance of the Truax-Thiel studies, headed that group. Vanden Heuvel was acting project director for the Air Force.

As the Douglas team headed home to jiggle space from the DC-6 and DC-7 production lines then going full blast, Mettler was pleased with the balance in the technical bank.

He was going to need it much sooner than expected.

8.

EMERGENCY SURGERY

Washington, D. C.
January, 1956

DR. VON NEUMANN'S Teapot Committee, the Strategic Missiles Evaluation Committee set up more than two years before by shrewd, Wales-born Trevor Gardner, was meeting in most extraordinary session. The call had gone out suddenly. The subject was the Thor. The scene bordered on the eerie and cast a stark black-and-white realism on the session, with no gray shadings to soften the necessity.

It was held in an operating room of Walter Reed Army Hospital.

The cancer that was to take Dr. von Neumann's life already was at work. He was hospitalized. For him to conduct a meeting elsewhere was out of the question. Yet even in these grave circumstances to be paralleled later during the last illness of Secretary of State John Foster Dulles, Dr. von Neumann was concerned more with the greater cancer that periled freedom.

Specific motivation for the Walter Reed gathering would remain an official secret for years to come. However, skillful fitting together of the jigsaw pieces of the moment, the open and covert international developments of the day, the probable content of Intelligence dispatches, and the patterned reactions of State Department circles, could provide a basis for an educated estimate. Tensions were growing in the Middle East. Some Nasser-guided explosion seemed inevitable, as did Soviet support for whatever course he might choose. Long-range radar screens on Russia's southern rim, near her known rocket-test centers, were showing significant pips. There was every reason to fear that the Reds were ahead of the schedule predicted by even the Killian report. Soon the Kremlin's threats of instant, total destruction against western Europe would carry respectable teeth.

At the same time, strangely enough, our most publicized crash efforts to stand Russia off with deterrent power—the Atlas and Titan ICBM's—carried the possibility of aiding the Soviets to alienate our valued allies, those Western nations we were seeking to protect as well as ourselves. The very nature of the weapons, able to strike Russian centers from the continental United States, was giving rise to fears among our friends abroad. Would the ICBM's mean a return to virtual isolationism, a "Fortress America" concept, and their ultimate abandonment?

In such a confused and dangerous picture the State Department obviously needed a dual-purpose tool. Russia's new threat must be met with a force she could understand and respect. Our Western friends must be transformed from passive to active allies. Basing the free world's first long-range, nuclear-warheaded ballistic missiles within their borders was one way, perhaps the only way in sight, of satisfying the multiple requirements.

Such was the speculation, in varying degrees and in varying fragments, running through the minds of the impressive list called before the committee at Walter Reed Hospital. One by one they arrived unobtrusively, identified themselves, and were allowed through the closely guarded doors to the gleaming amphitheater. All were top level: Defense Secretary Wilson, General Power of ARDC, General Schriever of BMD, and Dr. Si Ramo of STL's parent Ramo-Wooldridge Corporation were representative. All knew the questions the Von Neumann committee wanted answered that day: "Can Thor be ready sooner than the January, 1960, operational date given the newly selected prime contractor little more than a month age? How much sooner? When could they expect the first successful R & D flight of a bird? When would the first operational configuration be test-flown?"

Rube Mettler, as STL's focal point of all information intake on the status and outlook for every part, component, and subsystem, was elected to do the briefing.

It was a very grave responsibility. Thor's final weight had just been determined. The Atlantic Missile Range was instrumented only for relatively slow aerodynamic missiles, such as the subsonic Northrop Snark, not for ballistic missiles. The nose cone was a wooden dummy and a set of calculations on paper; would it stand up to the heat of re-entry as expected? The X-17 re-entry-test vehicles, for that specific purpose, had been authorized but the first would not be flown for three months.

Overriding even these factors was the advance warning

that the dates asked were needed at the highest levels of government; that they would be used in discussions with our allies and in diplomacy with the Russians. The most sobering note of all was that the missilemen were asked, tacitly but unmistakably, to commit their professional reputations to the dates given.

Rube Mettler knew they all were sticking their necks out. He took a last mental look at his "money in the bank" and laid down a new schedule: The first launching attempt of a Thor would be accomplished by the end of 1956 and the first full-range R & D flight by July, 1957.

The first combat configuration of Thor would be launched exactly one year later, in July, 1958.

And the first operational firing by troops would be written into the record by July, 1050. . . .

As quietly as they had arrived, the members of the group slipped away from Walter Reed Hospital, each of those directly concerned with Thor bearing a new burden of responsibility.

9.

NESTS FOR THE BIRDS

February, 1956

THE drive for concurrency already was beginning to produce some unanticipated by-products. Douglas put it on record that they intended to have the first Thor flight-test vehicle off the production line by midautumn. Over the Hollywood Hills and Santa Monica Mountains to the north, in San Fernando Valley, Rocketdyne's Sam Hoffman was determined that if Douglas came through, his company's rocket engines would not be a delaying factor in the program. The competitive drive to beat the schedule was contagious. It was picked up at AC Spark Plug and at GE for the nose cone. Thousands of people across the nation were finding themselves in the same situation as STL's Dolph Thiel. He then chiefly was monitoring the Douglas effort, helping check drawings that were still "hot," then rushing them down to the production people in the big bay on the plant's southwest reaches, by the runway at Clover Field.

Each succeeding day became longer, each night at home shorter, less frequent, until this pattern evolved for many responsible engineers in the year ahead: four hours' sleep per night on the average, with a large, uncounted percentage of it on airplanes, scurrying back and forth across the land to pull in loose edges here, add impetus there.

Over at BMD in Inglewood, too, things were shaking down to a routine of the urgent and unexpected. Colonel Ed Hall, a propulsion expert who took his degrees from the College of the City of New York and the California Institute of Technology, was about to be named first Thor project director. Lieutenant Colonel Francis J. (Joe) Hale, to become his deputy, had been on the roster for a month. Vanden Heuvel, after his over-all stewardship of the initial days, was about to take on the ground support equipment (GSE) task, biggest element in any long-range ballistic missile program. Lieutenant Colonel (later Colonel) Richard K. Jacobson, General Schriever's assistant commander for missile tests, was already planning for the ultimate series of Atlas, later Titan, launchings from Cape Canaveral, Florida.

And there was the problem of flight tests for Thor.

The tightened schedule meant that the first Thor IRBM would have to roar off the launching pad down the Atlantic range six months before the first scheduled, abbreviated journey of an Atlas ICBM. But there was no pad. No long-range ballistic missile ever had been fired from Florida. There was nothing to record ballistic impact 1,750 miles away.

Cape Canaveral still was much what it had been nine years before, when it was selected as an R & D missile launching site. It consisted of fifteen thousand acres of palmetto and rattlesnakes on a wedge of sand scarcely above high tide hooking into the Atlantic from Florida's midriff. It jutted out, then up slightly, from the barrier strip of land that clings to Florida's east coast like a form-fitting skirt, separated from the mainland by the blue slip of the Banana River. The biggest venture reflected in current construction was the launching complex for Army's two-hundred-mile-range Redstone surface-to-surface missile.

The key representatives of the organizations most concerned, BMD, STL, and Douglas, the last charged with conducting the flight tests as well as airframe construction and missile assembly under their prime contract, boarded planes for the first of a seemingly endless series of flights to Canaveral. They learned immediately that this was a tedious, frustrating factor in the Thor program. Commercial air routes between Los Angeles and "the Cape" in 1956, and for years later, were found to remind one of the ancient story about the traveling salesman asking directions of the farmer, and finally getting the answer, "Well, truth is, you just can't get there from here." Twenty hours of doglegging and plane changing was the rule rather than the exception.

BMD pulled a C-118 transport from the MATS inventory and established a regular coast-to-coast airlift operated by private concerns under fixed-cost contracts. It was called "Hebner's Airline" for the colonel who set it up, and "Red-eye Express" for the tired passengers who climbed out at one end or the other of the line after the still-lengthy flights.

None needed those extra air hours to reflect on the urgency of obtaining launching facilities. The basic flight-test program already was laid down in four major phases.

Phase One, from the engineering standpoint, was designed to prove out the basic compatibility of the Thor's airframe, engine, and autopilot. Many missiles would be launched in this phase. Even seeming "failures" would telemeter back vital data. But from the political standpoint, it was extremely critical to fire one the full range at the earliest date. Miles of data could not supplant that single, prestige-packed fact in selling Thor to our allies and hurling it diplomatically in the face of our potential enemies.

Phase Two would find AC Spark Plug's AChiever all-inertial guidance system ready to join the growingly complex system controlled in flight to that point.

Phase Three would add the final element of the GE nose cone and its carefully shielded payload, the thermonuclear warhead. In this case, it would be a dummy provided by the Atomic Energy Commission (AEC) of precisely the same size, weight, mass, and center of gravity as the real thing, and quite capable of proving every needed point in flight, re-entry, and impact. Fuzing was done by the Air Force.

Phase Four constituted confidence and reliability firings.

With the first launching of Phase One planned for December, to start progressive flight testing toward the first full-range firing that had been promised in the Walter Reed Hospital meeting for July, 1957, with nothing done at Canaveral except some sand-scraping by bulldozers, and with normal construction routine indicating that it would take fourteen months to build a complex, it is small wonder that nearly everyone concerned privately believed everyone else was mad.

That, he would admit much later, was the reaction of Joe Hale when he had arrived at BMD in January fresh from the "normal times" of traditional step-by-step development programs. "Nothing on the drawing boards, and we're going to fire within a year?" he mused. "This is ridiculous!"

The same feeling was held initially, and also privately, by another officer who would play an increasingly greater role in the Thor program as the years swept by. He was Colonel Jacobson, thereafter so widely known as "Colonel Jake" that it is probable the nickname will stick when he receives the general officer rank toward which he seems to be inevitably heading.

Colonel Jake had been on TDY for some time to Patrick Air Force Base, nerve center of the Air Force Missile Test Center (AFMTC) eighteen miles south of Canaveral on the long shaft of sand. He too had looked at the programs in the early stages of the accelerated ICBM's and told himself, "I'm not going with *that* bunch of troops. They've lost their heads. It can't possibly be done."

Both, however, took a sober look at one additional point. The Air Force was committed to the schedules. They shook off their disbelief and buckled into the job of meeting them. In short, they also became madmen in the eyes of those officers and civilians joining the ballistic missile team subsequently.

This was a relatively easy matter for Colonel Jake. Possessed of an intense, driving personality that burns clearly through his dark eyes, Colonel Jake had arrived at Patrick AFB a year earlier with the request for ten launching stands and six assembly buildings at Cape Canaveral for the ballistic missile program. Earlier estimates called for only two stands and one building. The explosion that followed did not dismay the balding thirty-five-year-old chief of BMD's Test Branch. Alabama-born, a graduate of Howard College at Birmingham, and holder of a master's degree from Massachusetts Institute of Technology, he was a pathfinder pilot in the lead group at Normandy, in the invasion of southern France, in Holland, and in the Rhine crossing. His most recent task was installing atomic bombs and warheads in piloted and pilotless aircraft. Neither words nor rank daunted him, especially when he knew what "the boss," Bennie Schriever, back in Inglewood, wanted.

Hence, the sand already was being scraped for Complex 17-B at Canaveral when Dolph Thiel brought the first delegation to Patrick AFB in mid-February to meet with Jacobson, the AFMTC people, and the Army Corps of Engineers, who would do the "brick and mortar" work of launching-pad construction.

There was a hitch immediately, however, from Colonel Jake's viewpoint. He had anticipated that the Californians would carry with them the blockhouse designs, at least rough sketches to provide a basis for discussion. He did not know there had been no time to prepare them; everyone was starting from scratch.

"We can't afford the time to make a blockhouse design," Thiel said, "because we want to launch somewhere between November and January. Let's look around at what blockhouse designs are available already."

Colonel Jake was not one to spend time looking around, however, when a solution was at hand.

"There's a blockhouse down here all designed, for the Redstone," he said. "Borrow a set of Redstone plans and build it like that."

Thiel looked at it, visualizing the wall-to-wall banks of panels that would be required in the countdown phases of a heavily instrumented R & D Thor launching.

"It's a little crowded," he concluded, "but we can adapt it."

That, of course, was not the entire problem. There was the matter of range instrumentation. A splash net (instrumented target area at sea) had to be established. The sun-splashed island of Antigua, where England's Horatio Nelson was based for three years as a young naval captain in the 1780's, was selected as the land anchor at the far end of Thor's reach. Lying some thirteen hundred miles southeast of Cape Canaveral, it would be close enough to the impact area so that alert "birdwatchers" of the future would be able to see Thor nose cones streaking back into the atmosphere like flaming meteors against the tropic night skies.

At Canaveral, too, there was more to it than the basic concrete work to be done by civilian contractors under direction of the Corps of Engineers.

All this would provide only the base for the checkout and launching systems, plus the shell of the blockhouse, reinforced against virtually any mishap involving an exploding or falling missile. Still to be designed were the checkout consoles that would line the blockhouse, the intricate wiring from there to the pad, the towering service structure, commonly called gantries, to give the launching team access to every part of the Thor as it stood erect, higher than a six-story building, before launching.

Dolph Thiel and the Douglas contingent hustled back to California to get this design project in the works.

There was still another nest to be considered. This was for the so-called "battleship" testing which was programed as a prerequisite to any actual launching.

The name derives from the use of battleship steel, fashioned into the exact shape of the actual missile tanks so that repeated static, or tied-down, tests of major components—the rocket engine, its turbopumps, its gimballing system, its valves, the auxiliary power system, the response of the autopilot—can be carried out without the expense of using many actual missile tanks.

Initially three locations were considered. Douglas leased from Aerojet-General a piece of land near Sacramento, California, in the strangely ribbed terrain along the Sacramento River where dredges of the past century literally worked their way back and forth across dry land, taking a piece of the river with them as they moved along sifting gold from the gravel to the tune of $100,000,000. Another was at Holloman AFB, New Mexico, the third, at Edwards AFB, California.

Holloman and the Sacramento plot were eliminated on grounds of insufficient time; there just was not enough time according to the schedule to permit full construction of a battleship facility. And there were facilities at Edwards, on a barren ridge far enough into the Mojave Desert to be removed from prying eyes, which could be modified quickly.

It happened to be assigned to similar testing for the Air Force Bomarc (Boeing's jet-powered unmanned) ground-to-air missiles. Before long, Bomarc was boosted out of its nest for a bird that needed to fly.

10.

THE LONG SUMMER

Bikini to Great Britain
March to September, 1956

ALL hands were busier than they ever could remember that summer of 1956; so much so, in fact, that it literally could be said one did not know what the other was doing, except at the highest levels of BMD and STL, which were charged with making their concept of concurrency work. Generally, each phase was proceeding with a progressive series of dates in mind, trusting that the other components and subsystems would make their schedules and determined that their own responsibilities would not miss the preset milestones. Only in occasional events of transcendent public interest did they share briefly a universal sense of satisfaction or concern, as the event might dictate. One such event came on May 21.

That was the day on which Major David Critchlow, of Sacramento, California, piloted his eight-jet B-52 intercontinental bomber toward Namu in the Bikini atoll and dropped a new bomb from an altitude of ten miles above the Pacific.

He was scooting away in the opposite direction at war speed when it detonated close to the sea after a seven-mile fall.

The results were encouraging implementation of the experiments there two years earlier, for the efforts of all had been geared to successful development of the "bigger bang in the smaller package."

Most urgently needed of the subsystems was the rocket engine. Fortunately, North American Aviation's Rocketdyne Division had a flying start. While the Air Force Navajo program was cancelled out, it had given their team the invaluable experience of building the nation's first large liquid-fuel rocket engine, generating 110,000 pounds of thrust. This was the starting point for the twin boosters of the Atlas and, of course, for the single-barrel "half Atlas" engine of Thor. It is not quite as simple as it sounds, however. Building a pickup truck engine is not the same as building a power plant destined for the Indianapolis speedway, even though the principles of propulsion are the same. To tackle this new job of powering the Thor, Sam Hoffman, Rocketdyne's boss, and Chief Engineer Tom Dixon assigned Robert R. (Bob) Morin as project manager, with O. I. (Ole) Thorsen as his assistant and W. F. Wilhelm as project engineer.

Early decisions on the external fittings, such as where the lox and fuel lines would mate with the tankage, had allowed them to deliver a mock-up to Douglas in February, so there would be no delay in setting up the production line of the "bird." Then the real task of building and testing began, with the inexorable deadline of delivering a flyable production engine by September. Equally exacting was the demand that research and development versions of the same engine had to be test-fired successfully in the "battleship" stands at Edwards before the first actual launching of a Thor.

Technical problems competed with physical hazards in pressing for these results. Crews at the Edwards AFB site worked around the clock and soon learned that the nights were the danger periods. City-bred engineers became desert wise. After dark no one stepped from a pickup truck in the asphalt parking areas, or steadied himself by grasping the metal handrails along the walkways, without first using a flashlight for careful inspection—for these were the heat retainers, most attractive to deadly sidewinders seeking to warm themselves against chill night winds.

The dedication of the men at the test stands, as firings began in March and increased in frequency and duration through the blistering summer, itself could be a problem. One collapsed in a dead faint when he lifted his finger from the firing button after a particularly long run. Nothing serious; he had just been so engrossed he forgot to breathe during the more than two minutes the Thor engine was roaring in its tied-down test.

On still another day at Edwards, a test firing long in preparation was "scrubbed" at the last instant on humanitarian grounds. Just before the fire command, the test conductor took a last lookout through the thick blockhouse windows to the "battleship" stand. Sitting directly under the exhaust nozzle, nonchalantly scratching his fleas, was a flop-eared mongrel dog. He was booted on his way unceremoniously, to be sure, but there never was a doubt everyone concerned preferred to recycle the test rather than incinerate the dog in the crematory blaze of the rocket fuel. The dog, in fact, exerted more influence on the program than certain mechanical troubles.

In the early stages, for instance, there was a problem with the blades of the turbine fans in the pumps that drive the fuel, literally tons of it in a period measured in seconds, to the combustion chamber. The tips of the blades fluttered as the turbine rotated at tremendous speeds. The flutter caused the metal to fatigue at the roots of the blades. Then they would crack off.

The situation was diagnosed quickly. It was overcome by putting shrouded tips on the blades so that each nestled over the tip of the next blade. They were still free to slide, but the touching shrouds created just enough friction to "damp out" the flutter.

More important to the program, however, not even this problem slowed other testing. Rocketdyne engineers discovered that when a blade or two broke off a turbine fan, they need only remove deliberately the same number of blades directly opposite to keep it in balance and proceed with the test in question. Thus other phases of the engine program moved steadily forward, even as the shrouded blade tips were being engineered into later test engines.

That resolve to "push ahead with what we can" without halting the entire effort until one lagging part was corrected set a pattern that paid off much later when the Thor itself was put in jeopardy by a still undreamed-of crisis during flight tests from Cape Canaveral.

They had to be detectives, too, these Rocketdyne engineers. There was the day of the explosion in the lox pump. Everyone knew lox was tricky, touchy stuff. Almost no one knew exactly what combinations of circumstances could

RESERVE SUPPLY

The Thor in storage at Santa Monica

SHIPMENT TO ENGLAND

Thor being loaded into C-124 for flight to the United Kingdom

United States Air Force

**OPERATIONAL-TYPE USAF THOR
INTERMEDIATE RANGE BALLIS-
TIC MISSILE**

Douglas Aircraft Company

MISSILE #109. R&D missile leaving pad on successful flight

**MISSILE #101
ON LAUNCHER**

United States Air Force

MISSILE PAD AFTER FAILURE OF #101

United States Air Force

General Electric Company

NOSE CONE

The thickness of plating on copper heat shield is being checked
with special instrumentation

General Electric Company

TRANSPORT OF NOSE CONE

Thor nose cone is being delivered to pad

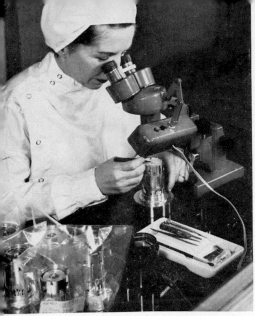

CHECKING GUIDANCE SYSTEM. Microscopic check is made at A-C Spark Plug, Milwaukee.

PROJECT ECHO. Douglas engineers and NAS technicians make final adjustments on pa load package.

TECHNICIANS AT WORK

COUNTDOWN. Douglas launch crew during countdown.

ENVIRONMENTAL CHAMBER. Thor engine Rocketdyne environmental chamber.

Douglas Aircraft Company

THOR SYSTEM MODEL   The display at Culver City

THOR IN READINESS   Emily complex at English base

Douglas Aircraft Company

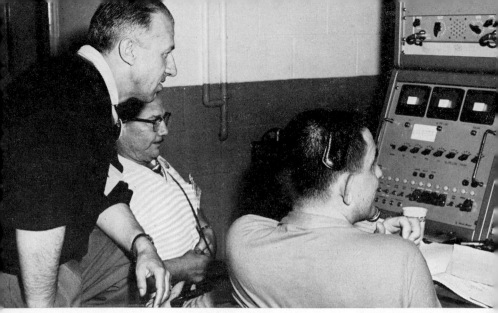

Space Technology Laboratories

ADOLPH THIEL AT WORK

MAJOR WALLACE AND TEAM

Left to right: Arnold Anchordoguy (STL),
Syd Greene (Douglas), Capt. Leonard
Farnung (BMD), Major J. W. Wallace
(BMD), Capt. Wilmer Walters (BMD)

BILL STITT AND JACK BROMBERG

United States Air Force

Douglas Aircraft Company

MISSILE TRA

THE LION'S ROAR
RAF Thor in full flight

(*lower left*)

AIR FORCE TEST CONTROLLERS. At the Satellite Test Center, Sunnyvale, California

RAF CHIEF TECHNICIAN

British Air Ministry

GENERAL SCHRIEVER VIEWS FINISHED SITE

Bill Duval and staff members briefing Lt. Gen. Bernard A. Schriever and RAF representatives

TRAILER TOWN IN ENGLAND

Trailers provided some home comforts, with forced-air heaters, showers, refrigerators

British Air Ministry

cause it to explode. All they could do was gather up the pieces from the desert's moonlike surface, speed them back to the plant at Canoga Park, and study them for clews. That time they were lucky. In reconstructing the unit the engineers could see where the burning started, its "fingerprints" seared into the metal. They could see where one piece was missing. It was simply a lock nut on a bolt inside the lox pump housing.

The next step was to duplicate the original conditions in another test, to attempt to create a deliberate accident to prove that the analysis was correct. In this case it was. At the high speed of rotation, the lock nut moved just enough to start scraping and scratching on the housing. The friction heat mounted. Ultimately the lox exploded.

More often than not, however, explosions destroyed most of the evidence. Then it became necessary to apply careful, logical analysis to the known facts, to winnow the possibilities down to three or four, then to settle down to painstaking tests until the defective part was singled out by trial and error.

Despite the unexpected roadblocks, the first R & D engine was handed over to Douglas in June, and the first flight engine, destined for the missile with "101" painted on its white nose, was trucked over the Hollywood Hills to Santa Monica on schedule in September.

This engine, and six more to follow it in the first "block" of engines, was capable of ample thrust for the early flights of Thor, before the weight of guidance and simulated warhead would be added to its innards.

Within the design remained one major undetected bug. Like a dormant disease germ, it would burst forth only when conditions became favorable. In a human being, these might include the stress and strain of abnormal exertions and sudden climatic changes. In the Thor engine, it would come under the impact of tremendous g loads of acceleration, and in the rapidly diminishing atmospheric pressures, as the vehicle flamed spaceward. Neither could be simulated effectively at that time in the earthbound engine laboratories at Edwards AFB or in Rocketdyne's own test station in the rock-rubbled canyons of the Santa Susana Mountains.

The first long-range ballistic arrow of modern weaponry was shaping up rapidly through the summer of 1956. Douglas was polishing the slender shaft. General Electric was forging the arrowhead in its meticulously exacting smithy. AC Spark Plug was working on the guidance feathers. And Rocketdyne was readying the muscle to power it. But an arrow without a bow is meaningless, and a ballistic missile without a launching pad is only a magnificently useless exercise in engineering.

Two types were needed for Thor, even as archers use different bows for practice and for hunting. At Cape Canaveral, the demand was for an extremely complex, heavily instrumented installation, so that the Air Force and each contractor could maintain a stethoscopic check of every component, both in the weeks of prelaunching preparations and, by telemetered data recorded on miles of graphs, during the brief chips-down minutes of R & D flight.

Since nothing quite like it ever had been built before, the original thinking of California-oriented engineers turned naturally to designs influenced by the familiar sight of shipyard cranes in Los Angeles Harbor. But these were vetoed promptly by the Air Force. General Schriever wanted something simpler, more functional, designed specifically for the task at hand rather than borrowed from traditional structures. He had a sound reason. Knowing that, at best, he would have many legitimate battles to fight at the Pentagon and on Capitol Hill in behalf of the Thor program, he laid down a firm edict: "There'll be no 'Schriever white elephant monuments' at Canaveral." The retractable "gantry" service tower resulted, giving the test crews access to every part of the erected missile yet able to be rolled away quickly and smoothly on its railroad-type trackage.

A harassing hitch developed here. The gantry was fabricated in sections at United States Steel's Consolidated Western Division in Los Angeles. Just as it was ready to be loaded aboard railroad cars for shipment to Florida, the steel workers struck. The service tower was caught behind their picket lines.

This was a job for Lieutenant Colonel Syd Green, and he met it head-on. Starting from the basic premise that the steel workers were loyal and trustworthy Americans, he met with the union leaders. Within the limits of security, Colonel Green was able to lay enough cards on the table to impress them with the national urgency involved.

Picket lines were rolled back to permit the shipment. The big steel gantry reached Florida in time.

The concept for the "hunting bow"—the launching system and equipment to be put in the hands of troops—was quite the opposite. Here simplicity was the keynote, for the operators would be GI's, not Ph.D's. Development of the needed operational GSE (ground support equipment) was delegated to Lieutenant Colonel George Vanden Heuvel. With his appointment in March, 1956, as chairman of the GSE Integration Committee, Vanden Heuvel's job was to direct the efforts of BMD, STL, and the contractors in their efforts to design, develop, and produce all the various support elements as an integrated package.

Even before the first research and development vehicle was flown, it would be necessary to start development of the training program and facilities for troops who would man the later combat version.

Together this constituted an unprecedentedly complex assignment, aimed at creating a system operable by average men after relatively short periods of training. To keep that goal in mind, Vanden Heuvel said: "We will assume that the missile itself will progress to a successful conclusion. As for GSE, we will start with a red light and a green light on a little box, and back off from there."

Colonel David K. Lyster, a jet-qualified command pilot who wears a sandy gray mustache on his lip and five tiers of ribbons over his left breast pocket, took on the task of preparing the operational data book. This was to project every item required to put an operational system in the field, ready for combat, and tailored for delivery to overseas sites by available aircraft. Before Lyster and the small group who would do the actual writing could start, however, they had to get the picture clear in their own minds.

The first step was to obtain all the film available on the German V-2 program of World War II. The British supplied some especially good movies they had captured. Looking at the events so many years later—scenes of mishaps, explosions on the launching ramps, missiles collapsing back in flaming fireballs of liquid oxygen-fed fuel—frequently brought laughs to the viewing scientist-engineers of a more advanced day. At these moments, Lyster, the twenty-first officer to check in at the old schoolhouse, said: "Those may have been pretty crude ways the Germans handled it. But remember they tactically and operationally deployed them in wartime. While the Thor may be considerably more sophisticated, it is a beast not a great deal larger than this."

It was a start. The necessary components began to fall into place on paper, in words. There would be a launch control center, a checkout station, a diescl-powered generator. There would have to be lox storage tanks—huge insulated "thermos bottles" to keep it liquid—and fuel storage tanks; a control point for the hydropneumatic systems; and lox and fuel transfer systems, virtual "Rube Goldbergs" of plumbing and valves.

By the very nature of the Thor mission, each of these would have to be compact enough to tuck into a cargo airplane, and mobile enough in itself, literally on wheels, to move easily from an airhead overseas to its appointed launching site.

Vanden Heuvel's Ground Support Committee, which included Douglas and STL representatives, at an early date set up ground rules to eliminate the possibility of mismatched units. One was to put the trailer responsibility totally with Douglas. The missile builder would make or buy whatever wheels were needed; the associates would be told what they were to put their products in.

Douglas subcontracted to Fruehauf Trailer, for instance, for van-type trailers, and the Food Machinery and Chemical Corporation for the great long semi-trailer to haul the Thor itself. It retained at Douglas, however, the body and chassis work on a number of "plumbing" units, such as fuel transfer units. A section of the Santa Monica plant in the future would look more like a truck factory than an airplane and missile plant.

Each unit created its own spider web of two-way communications and controls. The trailer-mounted electronic equipment group for the combat countdown was an example. Fruehauf built the van and Douglas fabricated three items, a storage cabinet, the van's heater air circulator, and the air blower for the electric equipment. From there the lines stretched out to the C. G. Hokanson Company for the air conditioner; to North Electric Company for the telephone connecting system and the interior loudspeaker; to Altec Lansing Corporation for an amplifier. United Control Corporation was to furnish the propellant loading computer, General Electric the power-distribution panel assembly, and Packard-Bell Electronics Corporation a whole host of items. These ranged from circuit breakers to power supply controls and a heater for the guidance gyroscopes.

Multiply these by the more than a score of individual units for each launching site, and a complex network soon is spread across the nation. Vanden Heuvel's committee—which included Gene Wilhelm and Arnold Anchordoguy of STL and Bill Hooper of Douglas—traveled the country for weeks, like indefatigable drummers of old, making sure every major participant was aware of his role.

Meanwhile, Lyster's team was preparing a model of the proposed site layout, using the facilities of the STL model shop. The matter of scale was no problem. "Scale it to the size wheels available in the model shop," Lyster said. "It'll save money."

There was motivation for even that seemingly trifling economy. The realization was just beginning to penetrate to the East that GSE, the part of the system that never would get off the ground, would be the tail wagging the financial dog of the Thor—and any other—missile system. The calls from Washington to BMD demanding estimates grew increasingly frequent.

Organizational changes in March, in one sense, made it easier to come up with quick answers. Parallel to Air Research and Development Command in the Air Force structure is the Air Matériel Command, the procurer of the physical things ARDC needs in order to execute its plans. As the sub-organization specifically for ballistic missiles development—BMD—had been created under ARDC, so was a parallel sub-organization for matériel support established at Inglewood. Known previously as the Special Aircraft Projects Office, it was expanded at this time and renamed Ballistic Missiles Office. Still later it would be called Ballistic Missiles Center (BMC) and for simplicity will be so designated here.

With headquarters in adjoining buildings on Arbor Vitae Street, the former time-consuming chain of command approach from BMD to ARDC to AMC and back again could be short-circuited by a two-minute walk.

But even the BMD and BMC officers were nearly as much in the dark on the cost of the strange new weaponry as those asking the questions across a continent.

Moreover, the question of how many to build was as unsettled, if not more so, than that of what to build. A directive in March from the Air Force Chief of Staff had called for the first R & D launching of a Thor the following December "on a maximum calculated risk basis" as a matter of national urgency. It charged BMD with developing and equipping and manning the operational units, with Strategic Air Command (SAC) to take responsibility for the first squadron after it demonstrated overseas combat readiness. On this basis, assuming American troops would man the Thor, BMD and SAC, meeting both at Inglewood and Omaha, hammered out their "initial operational capability" philosophy and concepts by May.

It was not known, however, how many squadrons would be wanted. The figure and thus the entire program, insofar as hard estimates of cost were concerned, kept changing. Those changes turned many officers into record-breaking commuters. In one four-week period Lyster made five round trips to the Pentagon. But the answers were put together in Inglewood.

Among the group working on the operational data handbook was Major William J. Murphy. He had been in the Matador program. There was enough information on GSE for this weapon, even though it was an air-breathing unmanned vehicle rather than a ballistic missile, for an admitted "gambler's guess" to be made on Thor GSE. With Bill Murphy's experience as a guidepost, the BMD-BMC team was able to "add a percentage factor here and a margin for error there" and come up with a basic estimate for a Thor squadron.

As the tentative number of squadrons varied, they simply applied the proper factor. When the decision came down to four squadrons, a fairly firm estimate of $100,000,000 for GSE could be made. Time proved it not far wrong, shocking as it was initially to those who had previously considered ground support in terms of aircraft engine-starter units and fire extinguishers.

General Schriever was having problems in another direction. The seeds of the Thor-Jupiter controversy, planted by the Department of Defense directive for two IRBM's the November before, burst into growth like bean plants in springtime.

The Rocketdyne plant was under Air Force "cognizance," meaning that the air service held the contract for its services and output and conducted the necessary inspection of operations within the Rocketdyne plants. General Schriever had assumed that BMD would receive Rocketdyne's full production of single-barrel engines for Thor, and scheduled his IRBM flight-test program accordingly.

A report of the House Committee on Government Operations, Representative William L. Dawson of Illinois, chairman, shows that General John B. Medaris's Army Ballistic Missile Agency (ABMA) "early in 1956 . . . recommended a second engine contractor be introduced for the purpose of developing an alternate high-thrust engine of greater performance and efficiency for the Army missile, but the Ballistic Missiles Committee (of the Office of the Secretary of Defense) twice rejected this request. . . ."

Its substitute action, initiating studies of long-range requirements for liquid-fuel engines, brought recommendations but no action.

General Medaris was left with no place to turn for engines

to get the Jupiter program moving other than Rocketdyne, the nation's sole builder, and to the Air Force, which had cognizance of the plant. With obvious and acknowledged reluctance, General Medaris "agreed to execute a Military Interdepartmental Procurement Request (MIPR) on the Air Force . . . for the first few engines needed in the 1956 Army program."

On the Air Force side, General Schriever assayed this situation as "a considerable risk to both the rocket engine development and to the Thor flight-test program." Nevertheless he "directed a paring down and rescheduling of the Thor program" to meet the needs of the IRBM Number Two program.

Seven engines had been allocated from Rocketdyne production in 1956, specifically for BMD's Thor use beyond those engines assigned to Rocketdyne's own testing program. General Schriever withdrew one more. The eight then were divided equally on an alternating "one for one" basis between the Air Force and the Army.

It was an unhappy beginning, auguring ill for interservice harmony. And the initial problem of the engines in the sprouting of the controversy was no more than the shaking off of the seed husks. Long, bitter, and divergent stalks were to grow and to branch in many directions.

The world was having its troubles, too, in 1956.

In June, in the face of internal and external pressures to withdraw from its centuries-old role as a colonial power, Great Britain evacuated the Suez, ending a seventy-four-year occupation.

Egypt's Nasser was not long in displaying his basically intransigent nature. The United States responded in mid-July by withdrawing its earlier offer of $56,000,000 to help in construction of the grandiosely conceived Aswan Dam on the upper reaches of the Nile. Four days later the International Bank advised Nasser that its pledged $200,000,000 no longer was available; it had been contingent upon the American loan.

In an act of dictatorial petulance, as it appeared his dream of a personal monument to rival the Pharaohs was fading, Nasser denounced the West and seized the Suez Canal. Moscow warmly patted him on the back as he proclaimed the canal's income would guarantee construction of the Aswan High Dam.

Certainly there was nothing in the world picture, even to the casual reader of newspapers, to lessen the need for the earliest, most forceful deterrent possible.

Under such growing tensions, Headquarters USAF in July gave formal approval to the agreements reached between the Strategic Air Command and the Air Research and Development Command on Thor's operational concepts.

In August, without public disclosure, the Army's deactivated Camp Cooke on Southern California's coast line above Santa Barbara was selected as the training site for the coming age of missilemen.

On the Air Force claim of 64,700 acres north of the Santa Ynez River, hundreds of millions of dollars would be invested. And Thors would be the pioneers to pan out there, in return, the fine gold of firsts in keeping the peace and exploring unique polar orbits about the earth.

11.

THE "TWO-BIT" PART

California and Florida
October to December, 1956

THE immediate pressures began concentrating on Cape Canaveral, building like a head of steam, from mid-October on.

In the Douglas plant at Santa Monica, the big overhead cranes that had been leapfrogging components and big tubular sections of tankage over each other in checkerboard pattern as progress here, delays there, were met in the production line, finally got their claws on a whole missile. Thor Number 101 had arrived at the east end and the big doors were swung open to the adjacent runway of Clover Field.

A big Douglas C-124 Globemaster, borrowed from the Tactical Air Command, was waiting close by, its combination cargo hatch and ramp hungrily agape.

Thor 101, shrouded for secrecy, was trundled aboard

quickly and quietly. The ramp clammed shut, the airplane engines coughed and growled into action. Within minutes, the Globemaster skimmed over the few blocks of houses between the Douglas plant and Santa Monica Bay, made its traffic turn over the water and, climbing to the east, put its black-bulbed radar nose on the course for Patrick Air Force Base in Florida.

Similarly, the engineers were converging on the Cape. STL's Dolph Thiel was en route to take up his months-long role as test director for the critical first launching. Douglas's Jack Bromberg, the test conductor, was on the way. Awaiting them at Canaveral was the Douglas launching team, assembled over several months by W. L. (Bill) Duval, the company's field station manager, who had been transferred from White Sands and Holloman Air Force Base in New Mexico, where he had spent nearly a decade in the testing of the Nike weapons and the Genie air-to-air missile.

As they welcomed Thor 101 and began readying the "bird" for flight, scheduled in December, every day's headlines, every newscast caught in motel rooms while waiting for sleep at night or shaving hastily in the mornings, emphasized the double need for Thor as a deterrent against Russia and a binder to pull the West closer together, basing among allies the same on-target capabilities as the Atlas would give the United States.

October 23, for instance, saw the Hungarian riots turn to revolt, to a courageous battle for freedom. It even seemed successful a day later, as Soviet troops and weapons left Budapest. But November 1 found the true nature of the beast displayed. Red tanks encircled the Hungarian capital;

three days later a massive assault was launched. What followed was systematic slaughter, carried out by Communism with arrogant disdain of the West's protests embodied in words, not action.

Almost simultaneously, secret State Department concern of months before—that the Atlas intercontinental weapon concept might lead to belief by allies that America would return to an isolationist "fortress" outlook—seemed to be bearing acid fruit.

On October 30, in what the late Secretary of State John Foster Dulles was to term "a complete surprise" to the United States government, Great Britain and France attacked Egypt, striking at the Mediterranean ports.

They had been building toward such a decision since five days earlier when Nasser announced formation of a joint command over the military forces of Egypt, Jordan, and Syria in the wake of increasing border clashes with Israel. The Israelis had attacked in force on the Sinai Peninsula on October 29, driving to within twenty-five miles of the Suez Canal. A British-French ultimatum to both sides came the next day, with a twelve-hour deadline: let Britain and France occupy the ports to safeguard the canal life line of those nations, or they would intervene.

Israel agreed. Egypt rejected it. Shipborne British troops hit Port Said. Israeli forces moved to within ten miles of the canal. And President Eisenhower, in the critical situation, appealed for a halt to the intervention, to let the United Nations settle the problems. All involved agreed, on November 6, to accept a cease-fire under the United Nations, with a United Nations police force to provide a buffer between

Israeli and Egyptian troops, and to have Britain and France pull out as the United Nations Expeditionary Force moved in.

The average newspaper reader might breathe easier, but there could be no relaxation at diplomatic levels. Great Britain and France had seen fit to "go it alone," keeping their plans secret from the United States. British-American relations frankly were at an alarmingly low ebb.

And there was a direct relationship between the events on the shore-line sands of Egypt and the shore-line sands of Florida. The sharp cleavage these events created between our allies and ourselves provided the poorest possible climate for our secret salesmen, seeking agreements for Thor bases of the future, for a weapon that was, at the moment, but a promise—and perhaps, until proven successful, a promise more of target risk to the nation accepting it than a bulwark to its security.

What was needed more urgently than ever was a successful launching from Florida, an incontrovertible fact that our salesmen in Homburgs could put in their briefcases to back their arguments.

People like Dolph Thiel were under no illusions as they began their work with Thor 101 and, in November, with Thor 102 on its arrival in another TAC C-124 from Santa Monica. Thiel could say: "We're working with people who never in their lives before have seen or launched a big missile. Our launching crew has never dealt before with liquid oxygen. We have facilities which have been built in a tremendous hurry.

There probably are a heck of a lot of butches. We have a missile built in a great hurry. It probably has some faults in it, some weaknesses. But I think the biggest problem really is the training problem, the training of the launching crew, to give them confidence and experience, to make sure they know what they are dealing with. This is a tremendous job."

His words were proved true at an early stage.

Every conceivable dry-run countdown was rehearsed again and again as soon as Thor 101 could be erected in the gantry on Complex 17-B. But finally came the day that a liquid would be pumped under pressure into the lox tank. It was to be liquid nitrogen rather than liquid oxygen, in a "cool-down" run; this was then considered necessary prior to pumping in the super-chilled lox.

Thiel, calling upon experience extending much farther back than that of any native Americans in the launching crew, was up on the gantry with them at this point. Remembering, he tried to warn them. "Look," he said, "when you dump liquid nitrogen or liquid oxygen into a fuel tank, it starts to slosh around. It makes a heck of a lot of noise. As a matter of fact, it even 'burps.' And it shakes the missile, too. So don't get frightened. There's going to be noise here, and the missile might even shake."

There are some things, however, that verbal warning cannot adequately prepare one for. The nitrogen did slosh. It "burped" resoundingly. Thor 101 shook. Just about everyone on the stand was ready to remove himself elsewhere immediately. The tendency to that almost involuntary response was written in virtually every face. But they stood their ground. And with each succeeding repetition of the noisy sequence, the subconscious urge to run grew less; familiarity and confidence grew hand in hand.

Countdown sequences, as such, no longer are a novelty to the citizens of the missile age. You have read them in detail, you have seen them in detail on television programs, ranging from serious documentaries to science-fiction projections.

This does not lessen their importance, however, any more than repetition lessens the importance of a preflight check list to the pilot and co-pilot of an aircraft. It is, in fact, far more important in the missile field, where millions of dollars ride on each one-way flight, where there can be no return to base if a minor element goes awry a few seconds after take-off, and where thousands of gallons of fuel and the "liquid air" in which to burn it must be pumped aboard, then used or flushed away depending on whether every item checks out "go" or "no go."

Small wonder, then, in those early days of learning, against a schedule of deadline performance, that Thor countdowns— ultimately shaved to fifteen minutes in combat configuration —frequently ran to twenty hours, and still did not reach the climax of engine ignition signaled by the onlooker's soon-to-be-traditional cry, "Fire in the tail!"

Each bug that developed, resulting in a "no go" report from the man at the blockhouse console concerned, meant finding it, squashing it before the count could proceed. Sometimes it meant recycling the countdown, going back and starting over. Most often, it was a tiny thing, a single connection, an almost trifling bit of wrong wiring. It would add phrases to the language. There would be the missile explosion because of the failure of a "two-bit" part; there would be the explanation blaming a "random failure." And when there were enough of these, the cynics would call a triumphant flight to target a "random success."

These sleep-robbing, nerve-jangling sequences became common in that December of 1956, with the time set for the first successful launching closing in like the walls of a torture chamber.

It still seemed possible on December 20.

The prerequisite of a full-duration "battleship" firing in the test stand at Edwards Air Force Base had been met. At Canaveral's Complex 17-B, there remained just a shackled-down FRF (flight readiness firing) of Thor 101 before the go-for-broke attempt to launch.

The countdown ran as smoothly as most. There were the inevitable bugs, but they were found and eliminated. It went to zero. But nothing happened. Thor 101 just stood there, the voice of its engine silent, lox wisping whitely upward from the vents as it escaped the frosted missile's hulk and expanded back into gas. . . .

Exhausted and disappointed, the Douglas test crew trudged back to Thor 101 as soon as it was declared safe. They soon found the problem. It was a "two-bit" piece that failed, a relay even smaller than a book of matches.

That ended any hope of a flight in December. The schedule was missed. The new hope now was to launch Thor 101 in January, then recoup by meeting the schedule of a full-range R & D flight by the following July.

A number of the California engineers, not needed in preparing the Thor for its next try, flew home for Christmas, chiefly to mend fences with impatient, lonely families.

And someone mailed the guilty relay to Bennie Schriever.

It certainly was not the kind of token of a Christmas-to-Christmas effort he would like to keep. The general passed it on. Today it lies among the paper clips, pencils, and scribbled notes in the middle drawer of the desk of Dr. Alfred ("Doc Rock") Rockefeller, Ballistic Missile Division historian.

12.

"LOWEST APOGEE IN HISTORY..."

Cape Canaveral, Florida
January 24 and 25, 1957

THOR 101 looked as if she was ready finally to take her first tentative dip outward into space on January 24, 1957.

The human element of the effort certainly was ready. Impatient might be a better word. "Let's get this missile off the stand," was the unspoken mood shared by nearly everyone. They had understandable reasons. Several actual launching countdowns had been carried out. For one factor or another, they had been forced to "scrub"—cancel the attempt—after tense, heartbreaking hours of effort. The only person who seemed unperturbed, unmoved, by delays was the Air Force RSO (range safety officer). And no one, in his heart, could condemn him.

The RSO had just one consideration in mind: what danger is there to life and property? Under that consideration, he and his staff wired in to the heartbeat of the missile in the same way that the blockhouse did, and also having instantaneous knowledge of independent movements on land and sea and in the air, held a final go or no-go decision over any and every missile.

Only a voice on a telephone in the blockhouse, the RSO frequently was, and would be again, a hated voice at the other end of that line. One such countdown incident ran this way:

RSO: Your X-band [range safety] beacon is a no-go beacon.

Thiel: You're wrong. Our instrumentation shows we have fine signal strength, and everything's OK.

RSO: Sorry.

Thiel: There must be something wrong with your ground station. It is a go beacon. We are convinced it is a go beacon.

RSO: No, it is a no-go beacon.

Thiel: Look, what are you telling me? Are you telling me that you're scrubbing us?

RSO: No, I'm not telling you to scrub. I am telling you I don't think this is a go beacon, and I would advise you to scrub.

By now the launching team was deep in the countdown. The money involved once more perhaps could be audited, but not the sweat and strain in the blockhouse. Nobody wanted to pull back and start the grind over again.

"Well, all right," Thiel said. "I think we shall go ahead. I think it is a go beacon."

Over the RSO circuit there was silence. But Thiel and the others could not help glancing at that phone now and then, asking themselves just short of aloud:

"What's he going to do?"

The answer came just before daylight of the perspiring

"winter" morning, some twenty hours into the countdown, and at "T minus one," just one minute before ignition. The phone came to life. And the RSO said with finality:

"We have a no-go beacon and are scrubbing."

Such was a bitter moment to swallow, but it would get worse.

Nothing like this happened on January 24, even though the countdown went on for seemingly interminable hours. Daylight turned into darkness. Thor 101 was picked out and bathed in the almost stereoscopic brilliance of searchlights.

Jack R. Gabrielson and Stan Raymond, Douglas photographers, were stationed with their six cameras atop a truck some nine thousand feet away. Like so many of the launching crew, neither had seen a big missile fired before. With no consoles to watch, they sat on the truck top and played poker to while away the hours, grousing professionally at their distance from the event.

When word that the shot was scrubbed for the night was piped to them, they did not know that the United States simply had run out of liquid oxygen at Cape Canaveral at the moment. Actually, they were rather glad. The delay gave them a chance to get back to Howard Maginniss, their public-relations chief, and complain about the distance.

The new countdown next day, January 25, found them happily closer. Their camera truck, just across an access road from one of the searchlight crews, was only twenty-two hundred feet from the tall white missile. When the lights flared on and focused their intensity on Thor 101 that night, the numbers stood out bold and clear.

Piped in to the countdown, they were ready for the sudden sear of belligerently orange flame at the "fire in the tail" moment of ignition. Like every other person witnessing a huge missile launching, Gabrielson and Raymond thrilled involuntarily as a rushing sound like a thousand freight trains swept up to their ears across the sand less than two seconds later.

But, being neophytes like the rest, neither immediately realized anything was wrong.

Then the searchlight operators began to run. Jack Gabrielson could hear their feet pounding on the roadway, even though his eyes were laced to the pyrotechnic scene a scant half-mile away.

Stan Raymond thought to himself, "It looks just as if the missile is melting down into a furnace."

But he still expected it to take off.

Then things, just bits of things, began falling out of the totally black tropical night sky.

For the first time Raymond noticed the silhouetted figures flickering by, hurrying away from the holocaust of oxygen-fed flames before him.

Jack Gabrielson started to jump off the truck.

But the thought flashed across his mind, "A guy could break his leg doing that in the dark."

He climbed down instead. But the instincts of a photographer reversed the decision. He climbed back up on top of the truck.

By then, on Launching pad 17-B, there was only the afterglow, really nothing to photograph. . . .

News of the swift and violent death of Thor 101 moved relatively slowly. The only "secure" telephone line, with a scrambler system to make gibberish of the conversation to any eavesdropper, linked Cape Canaveral to BMD in Inglewood. There an STL man, getting the word, telephoned Hal Thomas, assistant Thor project director. He asked:

"Have you got a basket?"

It was like a blow to the stomach.

Thomas had been through many failures of varying degrees in his professional career, but even years later he could not recall one that hit him like that brief sentence, after the year of effort behind the launching attempt.

He hung up the telephone, then lifted it again and put in a call to his boss, Jack Bromberg, at the Cape, for whatever further detail could be gained by double talk.

"Did you have an enjoyable flight today?" Thomas asked Bromberg.

"It was far from enjoyable," Bromberg replied grimly, "and awfully damned short!"

There were a few more words. Bromberg underscored the failure finally by saying, "It was the lowest apogee of any trajectory in history."

Thomas got the idea, even though he still did not have the official recording of that "apogee," or "most distant point in orbit."

It amounted to exactly six inches off the pad.

Everyone sought for humor.

Dr. Simon Ramo, of STL's parent company, Ramo-Wooldridge, was in Florida. He called Thor 101's accuracy "a fifteen-hundred-mile CEP." They had hoped to measure the circle of error probability at target in yards.

But no one really laughed.

Aside from the missile loss itself, and the sense of starting over again with Thor 102 when there had been such pressure on a successful R & D launching with 101, already a month late, there had been other losses. The terminal room under the launching pad, where all the costly confusion of cables and connections for checkout and prelaunching countdown was centered, had been wiped out. Not only was rebuilding necessary, but they would have to install fire equipment not previously considered, in order to prevent a repetition of the loss in any possible future catastrophe. And 17-B was the only launching pad available at the time. Weeks of work lay ahead before another launching could be attempted.

Back at Santa Monica, Hal Thomas had a duty to perform.

Reluctantly, he trudged the distance from his office at the far end of the plant to the office of Chief Engineer Elmer Wheaton, up on the second deck overlooking Ocean Park Boulevard. Briefly he passed the word.

"Well," said Wheaton, his expression more gloomy than his words, "that's too damned bad. I hope the customer isn't too dissatisfied."

With that, Douglas Aircraft and the "customer," the United States Air Force Ballistic Missile Division, went back to work.

The first item of business, of course, was to find out what had gone wrong. That was primarily a job for the team at

Canaveral, sweeping up the pieces, interviewing everyone who saw anything. That included the photographers, Stan Raymond and Jack Gabrielson, even though there was little they could tell.

"Did it appear to get off the ground at all?" Stan was asked.

"Not in one piece," he said wryly.

Gabrielson, a Naval Air Reserve pilot, came in for his share of the ribbing after telling how he could offer little because he was too busy climbing down off the truck to see much.

"The admiral," they gibed, "deserted the ship!"

The only happy people were those concerned with guidance.

"It was steering all the way!" they exclaimed gleefully, after examining the telemetry reports. "Six inches up and six inches down, but steering all the way!"

That was little satisfaction to the Douglas team, however, charged in its contract with successful flight testing as well as airframe building and assembly of the Thor. Even as rebuilding of Complex 17-B began, as soon as the metal cooled, the autopsy of Thor 101 continued around the clock.

13.

PICKING UP THE PIECES

Florida, Bermuda, and London
Spring, 1957

PEOPLE at all levels were picking up the pieces. There was eight weeks' work at Canaveral, putting launching pad 17-B back in order. Washington and London were seeking urgently, desperately, to shore up the bridge of understanding between the English-speaking peoples, so shaken by events in the Middle East. They were equally delicate tasks, and closely intertwined in some aspects.

At the Cape, there were things men could get their hands on physically. One piece of metal, for instance, had gouged a dishpan-sized chunk of concrete from the roof of the terminal building in the violent death of the first Thor. In the course of repair, new cement was poured in to fill it. Just before it firmed entirely, someone scratched in the surface, in grim missile-age mockery of the famed forecourt at Grauman's Chinese Theater in Hollywood, the figures "101."

Down on the flank of the building, where the steel stairs

lead up to the giant ring on which the Thors balance before springing up to space, a painter went to work.

In the tradition of wartime aircraft pilots and ship skippers who record their engagements with neatly arrayed symbols on fuselage or bridge, he painted the figures "101" high enough to allow for the many more that would follow. But, beside it, he also painted a graveyard cross.

The cause had been determined: contamination in the liquid oxygen led to a valve failure in the instant after lift-off, when thrust had barely exceeded the weight of missile and fuel above. Thrust "decay" followed. The torch of energy under the Thor no longer could support it, much less lift it. It settled back inexorably into its own flames. Lox gained added respect, and it would be more pampered in the future, under more stringent handling procedures. With those actions the Thor team put 101 behind them and buckled down to making Thor 102 work.

President Eisenhower boarded the cruiser U.S.S. *Canberra* in mid-March for a leisurely trip to Bermuda and a historic meeting there with Prime Minister Harold Macmillan. It was hoped that the six-day voyage in southern waters, down where the Atlantic Missile Range was growing under tropic skies, might help him shake off a persistent cold and troublesome cough before settling down to the task of mending British-American relations. There was much more than the proximity to the range, however, to turn his thoughts to Thor on that trip. While remaining nameless in the communiqué to follow, Thor was high on the agenda.

The prime concern was to re-establish a firm accord that

the nations would face the future together even though, as one writer put it aptly, not always in step. Problems must be met jointly within the framework of the North Atlantic Treaty Organization. There must be no need for Britain to "go it alone" again in the Middle East. And the United Kingdom, admittedly considerably behind the United States in missile research, should have weapons to give her a deterrent capability in the bigger East-West picture so that the United States would not have to go it alone there.

President Eisenhower wisely took an attitude similar to the Thor team almost immediately after disembarking at Hamilton and hurrying on to the Mid Ocean Club at Tucker's Town, where the private sessions would be held.

While broad areas of agreement had been hammered out secretly at diplomatic levels in the preceding weeks, as is customary before heads-of-state meetings, the British delegation was plainly worried over the President's personal temper on the subject of the Egyptian invasion.

Their relief was evident when his first private words to Macmillan included, in gist, this sentence: "We are not here to talk about spilt milk. Let's face our problems together from here on."

The complexity of achieving that, however, was indicated by the roles of the men present in Tucker's Town to complete an agreement sharing America's missile program, with its capability of delivering nuclear warheads. They included Secretary of State Dulles, British Foreign Secretary Selwyn Lloyd, Atomic Energy Commission Chairman Lewis Strauss, Air Secretary Donald Quarles, and Robert Murphy, the State Department's political expert.

Despite the United States law forbidding the release of

nuclear warheads to other nations, the work was complete by March 24, when an eleven-point agreement was announced. Prominent among them was one reading: "Agreement in principle that in the interest of mutual defense and mutual economy certain guided missiles will be made available by the United States to British forces."

In the arena of the press conference this was spelled out to mean missiles of 1,500-mile range. Those familiar with the program added mentally two words: ballistic and Thor.

Prime Minister Macmillan acknowledged that Britain thus would become the free world's first nuclear attack target, but he smiled and said, "You know, we can't help being that anyway." It was pointed out, without mentioning the ingenious "two keys" system that would eventuate, that the United States would be allowed to keep atomic warheads in Britain and to attach them to the unnamed missiles in the event of war. But it was noted also that the United States already had atomic warheads in England for the SAC bomber fleet. And Macmillan, ready to head home for the traditional British public examination of any major move, stressed the deterrent aspect of the arrangement. Were they ever used, he said, "it would mean the failure of all the purposes for which they were devised and invented."

The economic factor also was stressed. The missiles with their readily available nuclear warheads not only would save Britain development costs but also would strengthen her military posture at a time when it was necessary to cut the United Kingdom's commitments in military manpower.

And a few days later in London, on April 4, Defense Minister Duncan Sandys issued a White Paper touching upon the "economic strain" of cold-war requirements and acknowledging that "the free world is today dependent for its protection upon the nuclear capacity of the United States."

This document came close to actual identification of the Thor for the first time, noting that Britain's V-Bomber fleet, the counterpart of America's SAC, would "be supplemented by ballistic rockets from the United States."

Sandys also advanced a basis for greater independence in the future in the matter of weaponry with the announcement that Britain had perfected a "megaton weapon" which was to be tested and that "thereafter a stock will be manufactured."

But, for the moment, the Thor and American-controlled nuclear warheads were the best bet for peace.

When Mr. Eisenhower had climbed aboard the Presidential airplane, the *Columbine*, on March 24 to return to Washington—the *Canberra* was standing by, but the prospect of cloudy weather and choppy seas forced the change in plans —he carried a gift with him.

Mrs. A. J. Elmhirst, an Englishwoman living in Bermuda, had engraved a crystal bowl with portraits of Mr. Eisenhower and the Prime Minister, and Mr. Macmillan had presented it to him as a keepsake of the Bermuda conference.

At Cape Canaveral the Air Force and contractor crews, just starting to ready Thor 102 for preflight tests, might well have wished their chief executive could have looked into that crystal and warned them of the freak events and wry fate in store for 102.

The crew for 102 had grown in direct proportion to the pressures for its success. For instance, Hal Thomas, assistant project director for Douglas, had flown down from Santa Monica. But there was no inverse shortening of the countdown. This time power troubles were plaguing them all through the day. The count had gone to more than twenty hours, and the searchlights long since had been turned on the silent Thor. It was then, late in the terminal count, that everything went out: emergency power, utilities.

Scrubbing seemed unavoidable again, but no one quite wanted to give up without a last look at the problem. Two Douglas men, Ken Young and Bill Stitt, hustled from the blockhouse through the dark oven of the night outside to the on-site substation. A circuit breaker had been blown open.

A moment later their companions were reasonably sure they had taken leave of their senses. Young and Stitt gathered up all the desk-type electric fans they could find, then added a most amazing ingredient to their repair kit: a broomstick.

With the broomstick they propped the circuit breaker handle in the closed position. The fans were trained on it to keep the circuit breaker from burning up. And the count resumed.

Within thirty minutes they were down to the last items.

"T minus fifty seconds."

"Liquid-oxygen bleed valves closed!"

"T minus forty seconds ... thirty seconds ... twenty seconds ..."

At fifteen seconds, the diminishing count went into second-by-second sequence until the cries: "Ignition!" "Lift off!"

But they all had been that far before with Thor 101. What would happen now? The mounting "T plus" call of seconds kindled cautious hope. Then it became enthusiasm.

"Looking good!"

A few seconds more and: "Looks good!"

The count climbed, thirty seconds, thirty-five, and Thor

102 climbed with it. The radar plot in the launching block-house showed that the mighty vehicle was leaning out toward the Atlantic range as programed. But then: "Destruct!"

The range safety officer, watching his own radar plot, had punched a button. The radio signal ignited the primer-cord destruct mechanism. Thor 102's spaceboat hull was blown apart at the seams and engulfed in lox-fed flames above the water. The pieces came tumbling down.

That was on April 19, 1957.

What had happened? The answer was so simple as to be heartbreaking.

Somehow there had been a mix-up in the wiring to the RSO's console, a reversal of polarity. When Thor 102 speared upward, then started climbing out toward its prescribed course over the ocean, it looked like the opposite to the officer with the "life or death" power. It appeared to be heading inland instead, over the sleeping peninsula of Florida. He did what he had to do and destroyed the missile.

Once this was understood, R. L. Johnson could put it in words for all of them. "We've got a pretty good basic design," he said, "or it wouldn't have flown as long as it did before he blew it up."

Hal Thomas even added a bit of cheer. "I'll never forget that damned broomstick. It may have saved the program."

And the painter went to work on the side of the concrete walled terminal building, putting "102" just under the "101." This time, instead of a graveyard cross, he painted a small white missile beside the figures.

As far as Douglas was concerned, they had a good one, even though there seemed little in the event to inspire confidence by the British in the weapon planned for their country-side, or among American congressmen and top-level Pentagon brass not entirely sold on missiles as yet. That was one reason Bennie Schriever flew down to Canaveral for the scheduled launching of Thor 103 a month later.

14.

BENNIE'S LITTLE BAG

Cape Canaveral, Florida
May 21, 1957

GENERAL SCHRIEVER was a relatively infrequent visitor to the Cape. He would rather look a man in the eye now and then than peer constantly over his shoulder. Moreover, the growing number of ballistic missile programs kept him on the move, selling them, starting them, keeping them rolling. His airplane was his office almost as frequently as the pine-paneled space in Building Three in Inglewood. He has used the aft end of the craft as a briefing room, setting up charts and preaching the missile story when a high-ranking nonbeliever was aboard, a captive audience where a parachute was the only way out.

As often as not, General Schriever would be flying when a "shot" was scheduled at the Cape. On those occasions, as "T-time" neared, the crew wisely kept their distance from the handsome, thoughtful officer. Major Ed Tarbutton, the pilot, would monitor the radio for the result. With a mobile, broad, and ruddy face that should have known greasepaint, he passed the word by poking his head into the cabin and emulating either the Greek mask of tragedy or comedy, as the news indicated. No words were needed.

But Thor 103 was different. This was "a money shot." There was a lot of brass on hand besides General Schriever. Colonel Ed Hall, the BMD Thor project director, came in from Inglewood. Rube Mettler was there from STL. And again the countdown stretched out frustratingly, through the day, into the night. Three times it had gotten within minutes of ignition. Three times something registered no go, each time something different, forcing the launching crew to stop, repair the item, and recycle back in the countdown. Anxious as he was, the general called a meeting and told them:

"You've tried enough for one day. Let's go back to the barracks and try again tomorrow."

His concern was appreciated, but the consensus was to try once more. General Schriever, who had avoided the crowded blockhouse where he had no service to perform, went back to his motel to wait. It happened at T minus four minutes. Thor 103 just blew apart on the stand four minutes before ignition.

Major Dick Randall looked around. He looked into baffled faces. It just did not seem possible that the Thor would blow up *before* ignition. He looked into tragically unhappy faces. Rube Mettler was crying. There were tears in Colonel Hall's eyes. Tears were running down the cheeks of others. This was heartbreak in the extreme.

In the days immediately ahead, the reason for the freak explosion would be tracked down. The Douglas and STL people virtually locked themselves up until they found it, studying the recorded events of every console, of every countdown, until their eyes and minds ached. Finally it stood out clearly.

The warning signal was there every time. Something had been wrong with the main fuel valve. Either it had gone unnoticed or had been misinterpreted. Whichever the case, overpressurization of the fuel tanks was resulting, and the fourth time it blew.

Dolph Thiel managed a philosophical view of what he termed "the one black sheep" of all the Thors.

"It's an educational process," he said. "Something has been wrong with the discipline and the planning. When we go down to the wire in these launches, we've got to have tremendous blockhouse discipline and very clear procedures."

Procedures were revised and tightened immediately. They were set up to cover areas where there had been no procedures at all previously. There never again would be a T-minus-four explosion, and Thiel one day would reflect, "Thor 103 had a healthy effect; it paid off."

But that was later. On the night of May 21, 1957, the blockhouse crew less resembled pioneer missilemen than a ball club in the dressing room just after kicking away the seventh game in a World Series. The immediate problem was, "Who will tell General Schriever what happened?"

Rube Mettler took on the role of spokesman. A small, disconsolate group accompanied him to General Schriever's motel quarters. Mettler explained the failure. The general was the calmest man in the room.

"It's all right," he consoled them. "I expect things like this to happen."

Then, his mind already racing to the tasks ahead, he spoke again, perhaps more to himself than the others.

"Tomorrow I have to go to the Pentagon. And when they see me coming with my bag, they'll say, 'Here comes Bennie Schriever with his bag of baloney. . . .' "

15.

BACK AT THE RANCH

Ballistic Missile Division
Los Angeles, California
Summer, 1957

IT rapidly became clear that there would be no further attempt to launch another Thor—104—until mid-August or later, a three months' delay. This was extremely bad news to General Schriever. Pressure had been intense from the highest levels of government, from the National Security Council, to achieve the first "full-range" R & D launching on or before the July date set. The urgency was both political and psychological, since the schedule had been discussed in pre-Bermuda negotiations with the British. In fact, Colonel Ed Hall was in England at the moment, following the tragic loss of Thor 103, for preliminary "hardware" discussions.

Nor were these the general's only problems. In addition to the Atlas, Thor, and Titan programs, plus the WS-117L military satellite planning, another was about to be added to his already bulging portfolio of managerial migraines. These were studies aimed at a solid-propellant ICBM, eventually to be called Minuteman. The man to head up such studies for BMD obviously was Ed Hall, current Thor director.

Chief of BMD's propulsion development program prior to Thor, Hall was responsible for the earlier work leading to the liquid-fueled engines of Atlas, Thor, and Titan. With a new departure at hand for the distant future, as one of those who proposed his name put it, "It's more important to take Ed, with his creative thinking, out of the Thor program and apply it to the solids. There just aren't many of his kind in this business."

General Schriever agreed. But who would take over Thor, which had to be driven harder than ever?

The same type of analysis pointed straight to "Colonel Jake," then Lieutenant Colonel Richard K. Jacobson, chief of the test branch. And the same officer, himself promoted to general later, who put Colonel Hall's qualities into words, kindled a friendly twinkle in his eyes in recommending Colonel Jake: "This is the kind of character you throw out of your office automatically every three months, even if you haven't caught him doing anything to deserve it . . . but he'll get the job done."

Colonel Jake, in fact, did not even *want* to be thrown into the Thor office. It seemed that Thor was jinxed. The IRBM was a bad-luck item in his book. Called back to BMD headquarters and told of the assignment by Colonel C. H. Terhune, Jr., he refused. He waxed eloquent: "I've been here too long and worked too hard to be given a deal like that."

Next thing Colonel Jake knew, he was listening to the persuasive voice of Bennie Schriever.

"I'd like to have you step in there for 90 to 120 days," the man with the stars said quietly. "With your knowledge of the Cape, and the people there, and the testing area where they are having trouble, you could be of help to them. And I would appreciate it very much if you would do it."

As another general summed it, "Schriever is a remarkable gent for causing people to do things; he can sell 'em." Ed Hall moved into the "front office" for the studies on solid-propellant rocketry that would be recorded by the Air Force as the major contribution to early development of Minuteman. Colonel Jacobson took over the Thor program, feeling momentarily "like the officer who criticized the mess, then was made mess officer," but promptly brought to bear his boundless energy, enthusiasm, and talents.

Lieutenant Colonel Francis J. (Joe) Hale, who had been Colonel Hall's deputy, remained in that capacity with Colonel Jake. Far from being strangers, the two officers had been classmates in the graduate school at the Massachusetts Institute of Technology. Between them developed a warm and valuable alter-ego, "second-self" relationship. Much of Colonel Jacobson's time was necessarily spent in Washington presenting briefings, cajoling, insisting, educating, whatever the instant situation demanded, while Joe Hale was minding the technical store, readying the documentary ammunition his chief needed for the unending budget battles on the Potomac.

Other officers arrived to expand the staff, never more than a score at the peak, "back at the ranch" in California, as Colonel Jake called it.

One of those, who was to play an important role in Thor's

history, was Major Jamie Wallace. He drew the tough assignment of chief of the operations branch under Lieutenant Colonel Vanden Heuvel's Systems Integration Division. It was Wallace's job to ramrod production of the GSE (ground support equipment) for the combat version of the Thor, make sure the Air Force was getting what it ordered, and see that the nearly two hundred major items for each operational launching site would reach England on or ahead of schedule and, most important, would fit together as planned— even before the same operational GSE system would be completed and a missile launched from it in the United States!

The task was complicated by many factors. It had been decided three months before that there would be four squadrons, sixty missiles, in England, plus the training launcher at Vandenberg Air Force Base. Colonel Lyster, incidentally, had been on the scene at Camp Cooke since Easter. General Schriever had detached him from a Mexican holiday to plan the transformation of that Army ghost camp of sunburned, paint-peeling, sag-jawed empty barracks into the nation's first SAC missile base.

Under subcontract to Douglas, work on the various components was being parceled out across the country. But most of it was still on paper. The subcontractors, in a sense, were working in the dark, developing strange new items with no real idea of the whole concept into which they must fit.

Moreover, there was no final decision yet as to whose troops would man the end product. Through 1957, the plan would vary between an all-SAC program, a mixed British-American organization with United Kingdom troops gradually taking full responsibility, and full initial manning of the missiles by the RAF.

The overriding factor, however, was this: it was the first time in its history that the Air Force would take a product "in bits and pieces from the back doors of the plants, become transportation agents to move it overseas, and then say to the same contractors, the only ones who would have the talent to do it at the time, "Now put it together to our weapon-system specifications and prove you have built what we asked you to build."

Those are Major Wallace's words. It was such quick and keen understanding of complex problems that got him the job. From Wallace's performance in the Matador and other programs before, Colonels Jacobson and Vanden Heuvel knew they had the right combination of Solomon, Job, and Steve Hannigan—a highly competent engineer and patient administrator who could have succeeded equally well in public relations—to achieve the still somewhat clouded goal on time.

Under Vanden Heuvel's admonition to "get the show on the road," Jamie Wallace began turning things upside down. In doing it, he presented a formidable figure, with beetle brows as black as his mustache and a cigar perpetually jutting from his round face. To some who had not known him previously, who did not recognize immediately Wallace's deeply rooted Southern good humor, the impact could be terrifying. Among that group was young Captain W. C. "Bucky" Walters, Jr.

Walters, a slender, intensely dedicated officer who had been on the Thor project with Vanden Heuvel since taking his master's degree in industrial engineering at Stanford a year earlier, was assigned to Wallace.

There was little chance for discussion between them at the

start. Already fine-drawn from a year of effort in which he and Vanden Heuvel had been virtually alone on the operational GSE problems for BMD, and faced with new patterns and tempos under Wallace, Bucky Walters found himself picking up more pills than usual from the dispensary on Monday mornings.

It was about two weeks after Wallace's arrival that the captain came into his office on a matter of business. The major looked at Walters and said to himself, "This boy looks beat and worried. He's been pushing himself too hard." Aloud, he said, "Bucky, why don't you take the afternoon off and try to rest up a little?"

Walters did, but not long afterward another officer, an old friend of Wallace's, dropped in.

"Jamie," he said, "you're going to kill Bucky."

Wallace's black brows lifted. "What do you mean?"

"He's trying to keep up with you."

"That's not a requirement," Wallace said. "He has a good job and he's doing it real well."

The friend shrugged. "Yes, but he's worried. When you gave him the afternoon off, he figured he was practically fired."

Jamie Wallace called Captain Walters in at the first opportunity. With the inevitable cigar as a baton for emphasis, his face serious, Major Wallace spoke the piece that would make a valuable officer even more valuable, cement enduring friendship and understanding, and speed the success of the Thor program. In the corn-pone tones soon familiar from Los Angeles to London, Jamie Wallace said, "Let's have a very careful understanding. There are three things you can't do. One, you can't talk back to your wife. I've met her and she's too pretty. Besides, she won't let you. You can't talk back or raise hell with me, because I write your Officer's Efficiency Report. You can't raise hell with Colonel Jacobson, because he writes *my* OER, and that would make us both mad. But I'll tell you what you *can* do. I'll give you a full hunting license on Douglas at Santa Monica. You just go ahead and be as nasty as you think you can be on getting the stuff out that we want over there. Like any poker player, you can run only so many bluffs. But there is plenty of opportunity to use all your pent-up emotions on Douglas, and if you ever go too far, I'll get you out of trouble. Now, go get 'em!"

They parted grinning. Two years later, Jamie Wallace would describe "Bucky" Walters as a "supercharged, priceless detail artist" who kept at his fingertips every item of some three thousand tons of equipment destined for the pipeline to England. As for Walters, the number of pills decreased steadily, the tenseness eased off. The time would come when a bourbon and water of an evening would again be a personal pleasure, not a matter of envy.

Another subclimax also was approaching rapidly in the smoldering Thor-Jupiter controversy. Some faces had changed, others would change, in the civilian structure of the Department of Defense, but the question—which of the two IRBM's would be canceled and which would be approved for full production to fill the needs in the NATO nations around Communism's European rim?—went unanswered.

As far back as February, 1957, Defense Secretary Wilson said, "It's going to go one way or another . . . there is only going to be one of them made, not two of them." In March, James H. Douglas became Secretary of the Air Force, filling the vacancy created when Quarles moved up to the post of Deputy Secretary of Defense. Pressure, based on understandable human rivalry, industry nervousness on both sides of the issue, and a growing legislative concern that the dual path might be proving more costly than necessary, was growing for a decision.

Repeatedly throughout the summer, Secretary Wilson was pressed at news conferences for some word, but he had not reached a decision other than to give indication he was leaning to the Thor. Even this was indirectly expressed; he merely was not sure whether further emergency funds would be forthcoming for Jupiter.

In a move ostensibly to settle the matter with finality, Secretary Wilson in August appointed a special committee to "study the whole business and wind up with one missile." The chairman was William M. Holaday, Wilson's Special Assistant for Guided Missiles. But the desired outcome seemed doomed by the selection of the other two members. They were General Schriever for the Air Force and General Medaris for the Army. As might be expected, each supported his own system; each felt the other's had not been sufficiently tested to warrant eliminating his own. General Schriever felt that either missile would be acceptable, but believed Thor would do a better job. The stalemate in that area of the controversy continued.

August was a busy month in other directions. The first preliminary DEI (developmental engineering inspection) was held. For the first time, the people from BMD, STL, BMC, and SAC-Mike got a tentative look at what the Thor system would look like in the field. Actual components were not yet available in most cases, but mock-ups, in some cases models, were assembled to give a fair picture of an operational site.

This "try-out" was principally to reassure themselves that they were moving in the right direction, to obtain a glimpse of how the operational GSE was shaping up, and to give the Thor program management, logistic, and "user"—SAC-Mike— sides a feel for what they were doing.

Numerous changes resulted in items here and there, despite the rudimentary nature of the display. But it was extremely helpful, for instance, to the BMD acceptance team which had been set up by Major Wallace and would be headed throughout the program by Captain Leonard Far- nung, a highly competent man in a highly technical field. His duty was to make sure that each item was precisely as ordered before putting Air Force approval on it. There would be no time for changes in the hectic days ahead.

This preview also gave Jamie Wallace some unique ideas for the full-scale DEI in December, when the contractors would be called in to see just where their own "black boxes" fit into the bigger picture. For the moment he kept them to himself, perfecting mentally what would become one of the most dramatic engineering shows—and salesmanship efforts on behalf of Thor—on record.

If anyone even remotely harbored any doubt as to the urgency of the Thor program, it was dispelled on August 26. The Soviet Union announced that it had launched "an inter- continental multistage missile . . . a few days ago." It noted in threatening terms that this missile could be "directed to any part of the world." And the Communists topped off the disclosure, almost as an aside, by reporting they had successfully tested "a series of nuclear and thermonuclear" devices.

With Wilson out of the Defense Department post and Neil H. McElroy not yet in, it fell to Acting Secretary Quarles to make the official comment, "It is not surprising."

This was followed up August 30 by a DOD statement that the United States had known of four, possibly six, Russian ICBM tests several months earlier.

Few at BMD who could get away from their desks that day of August 30 even noticed the DOD statement until later. They were huddled around the teletype circuits to the Cape. Thor 104 at last was ready to go.

From the instant of ignition, optimism crept cautiously among them and swelled instant by instant as the teletype jerked out the story: "T plus TEN seconds ... going good ... T plus TWENTY ... plus THIRTY ... T plus FORTY ... looking good ..."

Up and up the missile climbed. The previous record flight, ill-fated Thor 102's thirty-five seconds of life before the destruct signal, soon was doubled.

"EIGHTY seconds ... NINETY seconds ..."

It seemed almost too good to be true. And it was. At NINETY-TWO seconds from lift-off, Thor 104 broke apart. The elusive, so desperately needed full-range shot somehow had slipped through their fingers again.

16.

AUTUMN'S HARVEST

U.S.A., U.S.S.R., and Space
September and October, 1957

IN any development program, certain missiles and certain engines are built that are never intended to fly. The crews at Cape Canaveral promptly turned to Thor 105, readying it for the next launching effort, but there never would be a Thor 106 on the pad there. That particular missile was built as a "hangar bird," to be retained at the plant by Douglas for structural testing. The same was true of engines. Rocketdyne kept a number for developmental test firings called flight rating tests, up in the Santa Susana Mountains. Eventually they were torn down and each part carefully examined.

During one such postfiring study in mid-1957, an engineering bug that would burgeon and grow later, fanning the Thor-Jupiter conflict and ultimately putting in General Schriever's lap one of the most critical decisions of the entire Thor program, first showed itself. Like many diseases, it gave only the tiniest hint of its potential at that early date; it gave only the slightest indication that something might be wrong with the turbopump that rams the fuel and lox from the big tanks to the burning chamber.

The nature of the weakness appeared to be "bearing-walking." There was just enough evidence of the bearings moving axially within their mountings in the turbopump casing to warrant a BMD/STL request that Rocketdyne look into it and seek some means of preventing it. But there was no great alarm. Telemetric data from the two Thors that literally had gotten off the ground, for thirty-five and ninety-two seconds of flight, disclosed no troubles in that area.

There never was enough telemetry to go around, however, in those early days of ballistic flight testing. Each contractor had scores of functions within his own component upon which he desired in-flight reports. Magic as the system was, literally a flying Mayo Clinic for missiles, cascading back to earth an incredible amount of data, it could not cover all points.

This led to the unique situation of buyer and seller in competition with each other. Normally, for instance, Rocketdyne would consider Douglas as its customer for engines. But when it came to the showdown meetings for allocation of the limited number of telemetric channels, the gloves were off.

Ole Thorsen, Rocketdyne's assistant project manager, for instance, might be fighting for a few extra channels, and a Douglas representative would declare, "We've got other things to find out besides propulsion."

"Yes," Thorsen would retort, "but if the propulsion doesn't work, what are you going to find out?"

Despite the fact some ears might turn redder than the Florida temperature warranted, the arguments were kept on a high technical plane, with all participants realizing that the others were unselfish in their motives.

And once the allocations were resolved, either by majority rule or, as a last resort, by Air Force decision as "board chairman," everybody was on the same Thor team again. Likely as not, they would repair to the bar at the Trade Winds Hotel, and seal the agreement with a "TD Special" prepared by the host, Tommy Daugherty. Everyone was an expert in his field, and Daugherty not the least of them in his, as he carefully scraped the pulp of the lime into the big glass and added the rum "and something else" to concoct his "Special." The host backed his product to the extent of taking one an hour himself. Most patrons found just two par for the course.

The Atlantic Missile Range, commanded by Major General Donald N. Yates, was building rapidly in scope and capabilities. Eventually to cost more than $500,000,000 in capital investment, with eighteen thousand people involved in tracking, data collecting, and analyzing and servicing the nation's many missile programs, AMR facilities were popping up like metallic foliage on the tropical down-range islands. The Thor, however, still was merely "shooting at the ocean" for distance rather than at any highly instrumented target area "splash net" for accuracy. The Phase One launchings were to test the integrity of the missile design and the propulsion system, and to prove that Thor could travel the distance required. That proof came on September 20, 1957.

Success was in the supercharged atmosphere of the blockhouse from the moment Thor 105 balanced momentarily on its roaring pillar of flame, then needled up into the fabric of the sky. On radio command, it found its heading for the "broad ocean area" below the distant horizon and accelerated toward ten thousand miles an hour.

Sooner than one sanely could drive an automobile the eighteen miles from the blockhouse south to Patrick Air Force Base, the inert dummy warhead had plunged back to the water eleven hundred statute miles away. The watchful, helpful Navy confirmed it. The full-range flight at last was in the book.

True, this was not the fifteen hundred statute miles specified in the requirements and promised to the British. But weight-distance ratios were clearly understood by the military and the engineers on both sides of the Atlantic. Stripped of the heavy burden of R & D equipment, the myriad sensors and telemetry instrumentation unnecessary in the combat version, Thor 105 would have gone fifteen hundred statute miles.

Back at the Santa Monica plant the news spread quickly. A grinning engineer, in the terms of his trade, estimated that "the sound level has gone up ten decibels."

It perhaps would have been more, but the elusive "full-range" excursion of Thor 105 merely confirmed what Douglas people, and BMD and STL people for that matter, had believed since the unhappily brief trip of Thor 102, inadvertently destroyed by the RSO: they had a sound bird basically; the rest was time.

Little time was lost in moving on to launch Thor 107 (you will recall that Thor 106 was the "hangar bird" retained at the Douglas plant), as the test team sought to speed the day General Yates could call his AMR truly a "shooting gallery."

The attempt was made on October 3. Recalling the unhappy fate of Thor 101, Thor 107 developed a malfunction shortly after engine start. It crashed back on the pad and was consumed in the pyre it kindled.

Colonel Jake was present in the blockhouse, along with a distinguished guest, Brigadier General Charles A. Lindbergh (USAF Reserve), there in his role as a member of the Scientific Advisory Committee. With the lox-gulping flames still soaring outside, Colonel Jake took a searching look at the "Lone Eagle" of three decades before. "He was the calmest one present," he told friends later.

There was but one bright spot. The experience with Thor 101 had resulted in extensive changes in the disaster precautions. Damage now was extremely limited. Within little more than a week, Thor 108 would be ready to go.

The next day, however, there was a new shadow upon the earth, literally and figuratively.

The Soviet Union, on October 4, 1957, launched successfully the first man-made satellite. Every 96.17 minutes the 184-pound sphere, big as a beach ball, circled the earth. At its high point (apogee) in orbit, 588 miles out, it was traveling 16,200 miles per hour. At the low point (perigee) of its elliptical course, when it plunged within 142 miles of the earth's surface each trip around, it reached a speed of eighteen thousand miles an hour. Moreover, it was talking on two radio frequencies, obediently reporting its internal temperature and what the Russians described only as "other data." They called it Sputnik, adding a new word to international language.

Psychological impact around the globe was impressive. Russia's propaganda machine missed no bets in exploiting it, especially since the long-announced American Vanguard satellite, a programed contribution to the International Geo-physical Year, still was not more than a grapefruit-size, 3¼-pound ball on the ground at Canaveral, as far as the public was concerned.

From the military standpoint and among the missile engi-neering fraternity, there was something more important in the historic event than the mere fact of a rather rudimentary scientific package whipping around the earth on schedule. It lay in the details of what else went into orbit along with the payload. These included the payload case and the nose cone. The total weight of the three items in orbit ran to four tons. A knowledgeable engineer with a slide rule could reach a swift conclusion: the Communists had a whale of a booster rocket that worked. The obvious corollary: the United States was trailing rocket development for whatever purpose, mili-tary or scientific. Just how badly, and how quickly the gap could be closed, would furnish fuel for political debate for years to come.

Thor personnel had no inclination for such debate. Their answers would best be found in deeds. On October 11 they fired up Thor 108 and sent it out over the Atlantic. It fell a bit short of the planned flight pattern. The engine had pro-vided its great thrust for a minute, two minutes, and more, right up to a second or two short of "nominal cutoff," the planned moment for engine burnout. It was so close, in fact, that only some "minor malfunction" was suspected. Not until months later would the telemetric record be pored over again, in the light of new events, for a thorough restudy of why Thor 108 cut off just a fraction of a minute too soon.

For this, it was later determined, was when the bug in the turbopump gearbox probably began to give trouble in flight.

For the moment, attention was centered on Thor 109. This was a special missile. With the perfect performance of Thor 105 and the seemingly near-perfect performance of 108, BMD was ready to push a Thor past its design points and impose even greater g forces of acceleration and structural stress than called for in the specifications.

If successful the launching also would provide the bonus of regaining some prestige for the program. It would not be publicized in order to impress the man in the street in Singapore, but it certainly would have a reassuring effect in government circles on the banks both of the Potomac and the Thames.

Everything unnecessary to flight was stripped from the missile. It was trimmed down to even less weight than the forecast figures for the operational Thor. Then on October 24 it was launched on a flight that took a little longer to arch into space and back to the sea than did the "full-range" effort of scarcely a month before.

For Thor 109 traveled 2,350 nautical (approximately 2,700 statute) miles!

There was no doubt that Phase One requirements had been met. The Thor had demonstrated range capability, structural integrity, and the competence of its control systems. It was time to add the AC Spark Plug all-inertial guidance system and push on with Phase Two of the test program.

17.

READY AND "ABLE"

THE Russians struck again in the new arena of cold-war competition—space technology—on November 3, 1957, with the launching into orbit of Sputnik II. Aboard the half-ton vehicle, circling the earth every 103 minutes was a dog named Laika. The fact fired public imagination everywhere and, in some quarters, public indignation. The demand for some comparable space feat by the United States grew apace.

Within the United States Air Force and particularly at the Ballistic Missile Division headquarters, these events were taken more calmly. For more than two years, since October, 1955, BMD had been working secretly on a project called WS-117L (Weapon System 117, Lockheed) aimed at building satellite vehicles that would circle the earth from pole to pole. The first of these satellites, for engineering development and test purposes, would be called Discoverers.

In the words of General Schriever, Thor had been recognized "right from the beginning" as having the inherent, alternate capability of boosting satellite vehicles to space, where they would separate from Thor and be driven into orbit by their own engines. It followed naturally that Thor would be selected for the initial R & D work, by virtue of its earlier readiness, when WS-117L was broken into progressive development phases.

Certainly this would be dramatic. But the Russian feats caused more concern over weaponry than space adventures among military missilemen. For the moment, highest Air Force priority had to be assigned to the present and near future demand of the ballistic missile programs. The Discoverer program, to be followed by polar-orbiting Midas surveillance and Samos reconnaissance satellites, would have to take their proper precedence. That plainly would meet the urgent need for a deterrent force to offset the Soviets' aggressive ballistic missile capability which had to be assumed from the space achievements.

The immediate problem concerned nose cones, the button tips that would have to shield the nuclear warheads against the tremendous frictional heat of re-entry into the atmosphere.

Solving it also would concern jack-of-all-trades Thor, in still another of the many roles it would play in earning its reputation as the "work horse DC-3 of space" in addition to its primary strategic role as the world's first ballistic missile deterrent force.

Thor's own nose cones, and those for the first Atlas ICBM's, already were a settled and tested matter, even though actual flights down the Atlantic Missile Range were yet to be conducted on combat-configured Thors, and though the first successful launching of an Atlas, on booster engines only and without nose cone, would not be achieved for a month.

This fact was a tribute to the driving energy and engineering skill poured into the program by the Missile and Space Vehicle Department (MSVD) of General Electric.

GE's Mark II re-entry vehicle constituted "everything but the bang," everything but the warhead from the Atomic Energy Commission, that would go to target if the Thors or the first "Model A" Atlases were called upon to be fired in anger. Interior electronics and the fuzing devices for the nuclear warhead obviously are complex. This vehicle, in an Atlas, must be able to travel six thousand miles and more, slam down to target at 17,250 miles an hour as friction heat on the nose rises to many thousands of degrees, yet keep the vital systems inside cool.

Several approaches to the critical problem of providing a suitable heat shield, or nose cone, had been studied prior to the 1954 decision to go ahead with the ICBM. Once that decision was taken, the Air Force elected to use the "heat sink" principle. In this, the nose cone would be fashioned of copper. In theory and on paper it was shown to be the quickest, most certain means of success. The qualities of copper should allow the heat to "sink" in, be dissipated by the metal, yet keep the interior of the re-entry vehicle down to a reasonable temperature.

As noted previously, GE's MSVD had reached the wooden mock-up stage, working on the timetable for Atlas, when STL's Dr. Louis Dunn and Ruben Mettler dropped in at the Schenectady plant late in 1955, explained the Thor IRBM program, and said, "We want the same nose cone for it."

The new responsibility put a tremendous additional burden, both administratively and in the testing aspect, on GE. Many more people would be needed, but they simply were not obtainable in New York's Mohawk Valley. On the other hand, it did not make sense to operate two plants, at widely separated points, on the same project.

GE's engineers further felt, in the words of F. E. (Ed) Rushlow, who would play a prominent role in the nose-cone program, that "we are the guys out there on the thin ice of technology, the farthest out near the current. We know we have to build something that will come in at Mach 22 [twenty-two times the speed of sound, for the Atlas] and not do what a meteor does when it tries this."

Under those conditions, the question was whether to move MSVD or not. Which would best serve the $158,000,000 nose-cone research and development program, and the nation?

The decision was to move. Facilities were available in Philadelphia. In early 1956, some one thousand people were transferred from Schenectady to the new location, where personnel grew to twenty-five hundred.

From there on the problems were technical, finding out what would happen in an environment the average person scarcely could comprehend and which the experts could not duplicate precisely until the entire weapon system was ready to fire. George Metcalfe, now GE's regional vice-president for defense activities, provided the first leadership in the virtually unexplored field of Mach 22 re-entry. Russell Hall was the first chief engineer. Hilliard W. Paige, now MSVD general manager, was aboard from the start. Leo A. Steg, MSVD Space Sciences Lab manager; O. E. Enders, Mark II re-entry vehicle program manager; and Rushlow—all these and others joined in tackling such problems as fuzing the warhead on re-entry into the atmosphere.

The unanswered questions of heating at the edge of the atmosphere were another matter. Here BMD used a different approach, a unique rocket vehicle called X-17 and produced by Lockheed, ordered in quantity in 1954 when the extreme problems of re-entry testing were anticipated in connection with the ballistic missile programs.

In all, twenty-six of these were flown. The first of the three-stage X-17's was sent aloft with a scale-model heat-sink nose cone in April, 1956. These vehicles were designed to climb to four hundred thousand feet on their first-stage rocket. Then, as they turned over and started down, the second and third stages fired, increasing its speed to Mach 14 or 15 in dense air at some fifty thousand feet above the earth. This provided a close simulation to the environment of Thor IRBM re-entry. Within a very few months the survival capability of the copper heat-sink design for the Thor was "conclusively demonstrated," even before the first Thor was off the line at Douglas.

Extrapolation of X-17 data also assured that, in the continuing testing, the same copper nose cones would serve for the Atlas program, which imposed four times the heat problem as the Thor.

These were emergency measures. GE, of course, went to work producing re-entry vehicles, the copper nose cones, for Thor and Atlas from the same pattern because the nation needed them.

Two dies were made. One was convex, the other concave, each exactly fitting the other; in trade terms, one "male," one "female." Each die weighed thirty-five tons. They were put into a hydraulic press with a fifty-thousand-ton pressure capacity. Records indicated it was the largest closed-die copper forging ever attempted.

These shields were designed primarily for the Atlas. Its "little sister" Thor, carrying the same impact but not intended to go as far or as fast, really did not need all that protection. But this was a matter of expediency. Later on in the program, GE started milling off a lot of the copper thickness of those protective cups, making the Thor nose cones thinner and hundreds of pounds lighter.

Those pounds saved, in curls of copper peeled off on MSVD's floor in Philadelphia, could do one of two things, or a combination of both: give the Thor more range, or let it carry a heavier payload its prescribed maximum of fifteen hundred nautical miles.

And those same problems—greater range, greater payload, or a balance between the two—gave rise to the problem under consideration at BMD in November, 1957, and the need for Thor to take part in still another phase of the ballistic missile program, as well as pay back some of its debt to Atlas.

Two months before, in September, 1957, technological advances in many directions, carefully checked out by BMD and STL, convinced them that the economic, fast-reaction, "rifle ready" Minuteman ICBM had become feasible. This was the program for which Colonel Ed Hall had been asked to study the solid-fuel propulsion problems, the Thor program at BMD being given to "Colonel Jake" Jacobson. One of the important aspects now, with application to later Atlas weapons and the Titan ICBM program, as well as Minuteman, was the feasibility of "ablatable" re-entry vehicles.

Contrasted to the heat-sink principle of the copper Mark

II heat shields, which "soaked up" and dissipated the heat of re-entry friction, the ablation principle proposed a heat shield of plastic-type substances. As heat increased, these layers would melt or peel away in absorbing the fantastic temperatures, thereby keeping the nuclear warhead and its fuzing systems relatively cool inside the re-entry vehicle.

It was much like being sunburned at the beach, with that top layer of skin peeling off, to reveal a new layer underneath for the next exposure—but all happening within instants.

This time, however, extrapolations—mathematical magnifications of test-vehicle results like the X-17 at lower speeds and temperatures—would not do. It had to be done through actual flights at ICBM ranges, speeds, and temperatures. Yet no Atlas full-range flight was planned for a year, not until November, 1958.

And there was a deadline of the following July to have the data ready in order to make a decision.

General Schriever and his vice-commander, Brigadier (later Major) General Osmond J. Ritland, had little trouble in finding the BMD team to survey the field of "available hardware" and suggest various "tootsie-roll" stacks of rockets to achieve the test ranges before any Atlas could. In fact, Bennie Schriever and Ozzie Ritland made a fine hand-in-glove team on any subject, with almost parallel backgrounds.

Ritland shared with Schriever the same quality of a soft-spoken but determined approach to any matter. Ozzie, destined to succeed Bennie as BMD commander when the latter moved up to command of ARDC in 1959, was born at Berthoud, Colorado, October 30, 1909, but was transplanted at an early age to San Diego, California. There he attended San Diego State College for three years until beginning an Air

Force career as a flying cadet at Randolph Field, Texas, in the depression year of 1932.

He, too, left the old Army Air Corps after "flying the mail" to become an airline pilot, with United Air Lines from 1935 until 1939, when he returned to accept a regular commission. After a brief tour at Hamilton Field, near San Francisco, Ozzie Ritland was sent to Wright Field for five years as a test pilot, during which he flew 125 types of aircraft before a wartime assignment as commander of the Assam Air Depot in India, where he won the Air Medal and Bronze Star. And, like such others as Colonel Jake, he was not unfamiliar with atomic weaponry. As commander, 4925th Test Group (Atomic) at Kirtland Air Force Base, New Mexico, from 1950 to 1953, he was responsible for the air phase of nuclear testing at the Nevada Proving Grounds, earning the Legion of Merit.

Their team: Major (later Lieutenant Colonel) Donald R. Latham, and Captain (later Major) John E. Richards, both of BMD's Armament Division. Simultaneously, STL's Dr. Dunn picked his representatives to work with the BMD officers. They were Dr. Richard Morrison, Dr. Robert Bennett, and George Solomon.

Together they conducted a thorough study and reached agreement quickly on one point. The first-stage booster would be a Douglas Thor IRBM. There was not much else to consider.

The second stage was a bit more of a problem. There were several smaller rockets to consider. But the answer was plucked right out of the middle of the Vanguard International Geophysical Year rocket structure, not yet launched.

They would modify the second stage, built by Aerojet-General Corporation of Azusa, California.

Thor would boost its two-ton weight off the pad and into space. Then the Aerojet rocket's own thrust, some seventy-five hundred pounds, would drive it solidly into the ballistic trajectory to carry it the full ICBM range down the South Atlantic and back into the atmosphere at ICBM speeds.

They knew the Thor was ready, and they knew the second stage was capable of the task. That's why the name of the two-stage combination was so fitting: Thor-Able.

18.

A TIDY PACKAGE

Culver City, California
Christmas, 1957

IN late 1957 no one was more disturbed over the Thor-Jupiter controversy, which had resulted in a cutback of Thor production to two missiles per month, than Major Jamie Wallace. He had, however, two things in mind to cheer him. One was the firm belief that there would eventually be an end to indecision, and that "all this would break loose" in favor of the Thor. The other was an idea to give fate a firm nudge.

Ever since the preliminary "in house" Development Engineering Inspection (DEI) in August, Wallace had turned his energies toward the full-scale DEI that is mandatory in any such program. This normally brings in the major contractors —Douglas, Rocketdyne, General Electric, and AC Spark Plug, in the case of Thor—along with the Air Force commands involved, for a final check before they plunge into production of the combat-configured missile and its ground-support equipment. For three days they would study the assembled results of engineering to that date, frequently in mock-up or model form. Then the "customer" Air Force, the SAC "user" of the end product, would order the final changes that appeared necessary before GSE production started.

Jamie Wallace saw it differently. Taking full cognizance of the political aspects, knowing that the specific shape and size of the Thor missile were about to be declassified, and realizing that the full picture of the operational GSE had to be spread to much lower engineering levels than the prime contractors, he came up with a bold plan. In gist, the argument he took to Joe Hale, to Colonel Jacobson, and finally to General Schriever, was this: "If we're ever really to take a giant step, we have to put together a DEI somewhere near Douglas-Santa Monica, bringing the missile and all the first production GSE together physically from all the contractors.

"Let the DEI run for twelve to sixteen days, instead of three, and bring in all the top-ranking people in the country we can get here, as well as the commanders, for a high educational value.

"We also have several thousand design engineers in the second and third tier of contractors, as well as among the major Thor contractors. Let's have 'Design Engineer Days' when these people, who operate on some little package somewhere, can come in and see this thing put together, see where their little package is fitting.

"Because," Wallace concluded, "if these guys, smart as they are as design engineers, don't go home and repackage or remassage this little box or that while it's on paper, we'll never get there."

Hale and Colonel Jake put their blessing on it, and it took Bennie Schriever just fifteen minutes to apply the final approval. On November 10, Major Wallace moved to the Douglas plant, where Jack Bromberg gave him a desk and a secretary, and he went to work.

Jamie Wallace went to work putting together his display. The first question was, "Where?"

Wallace knew he needed twenty thousand to thirty thousand square feet under roof, for the individual displays of the major component builders and for an auditorium big enough to brief more than five hundred visitors at a time. Additionally, six thousand square feet would be required outside for the full-scale combat launching site. Moroever, while there no longer would be a requirement to prevent the general public from a close-up look at the missile, the GSE beneath and around it still was classified. That meant walls or fencing twelve feet high.

A disused RKO motion-picture lot seemed ideal, but Jamie Wallace, realizing he already was building up the showiest DEI on record, needed only to roll that thought around once to reject it. "Too 'Hollywood' " was his view of the connotations.

Not far from the Santa Monica headquarters, however, Douglas owned another plant called its A-2 location, on the site of a former dog-race track in Culver City. The building was large enough for the indoor needs, and a parking lot had ample room for the launching site.

With a keen eye for the dramatic, Wallace sent up to Vandenberg Air Force Base for a small group of noncommissioned Air Force officers. None of the hundreds of official visitors due to attend the DEI would know that the dozen sergeants, neat in maintenance-type uniforms and metal "hard hats" with the chevrons and rockers of their rank, were virtually the entire missile force of SAC at that moment, the nucleus that would expand to become the First Missile Division and the teachers of RAF crews so soon after. For the major saw to it that each was briefed in the particular job he would man and, in turn, would be able to answer intelligently any questions asked about it.

The Douglas people pitched in wholeheartedly and with sealed lips. No one in the surrounding residential area knew what was going on behind the high plywood fence. At day's end, Wallace and a number of the Douglas gang would duck across the residential street to a little tavern called the Copper Kitchen. There they would have a day's-end drink, chuckling over the day's amazing accomplishments, and hoping the neighbors outside the fence had not seen anything to take the edge off the surprise awaiting them on December 3.

That was opening day of the DEI period, destined to run through December 21 and "play" to approximately thirty-five hundred people. And at 2 A.M., December 3, last-minute pieces of equipment, flown in the previous evening, were being emplaced, and Colonel Jake, the assigned master of ceremonies, was still in New York City on other urgent business.

The colonel caught a plane, however, made it home, changed clothes, and reached the A-2 plant in Culver City just as Joe Hale was finishing the introductory remarks to the first group.

The introductory speech, as with the many groups to follow, was given in the impromptu auditorium constructed in the preceding two weeks. There also was given a working demonstration of the operational site with a one-twentieth scale model. The next steps were a tour of the static component displays, then a visit to a simulated RIM (reception-inspection-maintenance) building, such as was contemplated for each Thor squadron headquarters.

The climax came next when the audience stepped outside to view the real thing, with uniformed troops erecting and lowering an actual Thor on its mobile transporter-erector as calmly as though they had been doing it for years.

The impact of this demonstration was almost as great outside the fence as inside. Startled householders, shopkeepers, and motorists were getting their first peek at the sixty-five-foot monster, which towered above them, then periodically leaned over gently again to disappear behind the fence. Telephones jangled. Tipsters called newspapers. The editor of *The Santa Monica Outlook* promptly hired a helicopter to take pictures—and Colonel Jake, Joe Hale, and Jamie Wallace were chuckling. It could not have worked out better.

The list of visitors was impressive in position as well as number. They included, for instance, Secretary of the Army Brucker; Dr. George Kistiakowsky, President Eisenhower's scientific adviser; and Dr. Theodore von Karman, who actually founded the present vast Aerojet-General Corporation early in World War II when, with a group of California Institute of Technology students, he developed the famed JATO (jet-assisted take-off) rockets for heavy aircraft.

For Dr. von Karman, as well as for virtually all the others, it was an eye-opening experience to see for the first time the impressive proportions of the ballistic missile project that the GSE constituted. Riding the area in a golf cart, the elderly scientific advisor to the North Atlantic Treaty Organization at first was commenting on the stately missile itself.

"The missile is easy, sir," said Colonel Jake, escorting him. "The ground-support equipment is the hard part."

Considerably later a Douglas scientist spied Dr. von Karman and hurried over to greet him. After the preliminaries, Colonel Jake chuckled inwardly as the doctor remarked sagely: "The missile is easy. It's this equipment, that's the hard part!"

There were a couple of rough spots in the long-playing DEI, but they had nothing to do with the missile.

The first crises came early. One of the Vandenberg sergeants was explaining to a general officer the operation of some part of the GSE when something plinked against his "hard hat." He obviously was under attack and reconnaissance was immediately in order.

A situation report came back promptly. Some small boys on their lawn across the street were throwing stones at the Thor every time it lifted erect behind the fence.

Major Wallace took emergency measures. He detailed another noncom, armed with ammunition in the form of cash, to find a canteen quickly, buy up candy bars and bribe the junior assault team away from their newly found hobby.

It was not until midnight that the major awoke to the realization that he might have employed a dangerous tactic. "Tomorrow," the thought flashed across his mind, "there'll be a hundred little boys out there, each wanting a bar of candy."

The other problem came as the calendar marched closer to Christmas. Jamie Wallace rationalized later that he probably got himself into it when he remarked casually to a couple of Douglas secretaries and their husbands one night: "Maybe we ought to put up a Christmas tree to remind these people of the date, or we may be here until New Year's."

Next morning there was a little four-dollar Christmas tree, lights twinkling among its decorations, in the administrative lobby of the A-2 plant. Under it was a sign reading, "Remember, it's close to Christmas."

The happy holiday spirit engendered by the tree quickly appeared headed for an unhappy end, however. A secretary warned Wallace that the chief of the Douglas security force was on his way down to see him.

"Major," said the plant officer, "don't you know you can't have a Christmas tree out there?"

Wallace, who had noticed in passing that it was a strictly fireproof variety, was taken aback. "Why not?"

"It's against company policy," the regulation-minded chief guard said. "There can only be one tree in the Douglas organization, and that's in the main hall in the headquarters building."

Jamie Wallace thought that over a moment. Then he said, "Well, I've been over here so long I was just getting homesick. I put up that tree because I was trying to get these other people to go home."

This time the chief guard was taken aback. He went away to think over the next move, then returned twenty minutes later and inspected the tree.

"Does it pass?" Wallace asked.

"As far as I'm concerned," he said.

The tree stayed.

The DEI closed down on December 21. It had been a good show visually and psychologically. Many believed later that it was a major turning point, playing a key role in the subsequent DOD decision to turn over operational control of the Army's Jupiter to the Air Force. But it also was a good engineering show, with 80 per cent of the production equipment actually "working" and the remaining 20 per cent providing exact duplicates.

Put together on a parking lot in three weeks, it forced things to fit together. This, in turn, undoubtedly eliminated in advance many later problems with the installation and checkout overseas.

After the house was finally dark that chilly California winter night, Colonel Jake returned to the Santa Monica plant to find a telephone call waiting from the commander of the Air War College. He had heard so much about the DEI he wanted to bring out the whole War College for a day of briefings and demonstrations.

"Sir, I would love to do it," said the colonel, "but I'll have to decline. We're closing up unless the Air Staff says we can stay open."

He explained that many parts of the outside demonstra-

tion were first items of production, and that to continue
would jeopardize the schedule.

Jamie Wallace was grinning as it ended. "Close down with
'em applauding in the aisles," he said, "and screaming for
tickets."

19.

THE BEGINNING IN BRITAIN

Los Angeles to London
January and February, 1958

JANUARY was a month of decision. Several teams had been working toward it, some openly, some secretly. The DEI at Santa Monica was one phase, with the secrecy lid off once the Thor was erected for the first time, tacitly inviting helicopter inspection by the press of the fact there really *was* a combat-style launching complex program in existence.

Down at Cape Canaveral, the Air Force-industry team had fired up two more Thors—numbers 112 and 113, the first launched with the all-inertial guidance system aboard—while the DEI was in progress. These, on December 7 and December 19, could not be hidden from the eyes of alert "bird-watching" newsmen nearby. But the results could. Number 112, from the missile standpoint, performed properly, but the guidance did not. It lost stability after 107 seconds of powered flight and was destroyed. Number 113, the tenth and final Thor launched in 1957, was a good flight all the way. The AC system guided it fully. Its impact point was verified by five hydrophones in the South Atlantic target area.

Each event contributed mightily to the effort of still a third team, the growing group of negotiators working secretly with the British in London to hammer out a workable agreement to get the Thors on England's soil as soon as possible.

Heading this team, as the one top-level point of contact with the United Kingdom's Air Ministry for final decisions, was an ideally experienced officer, Major General William H. (Butch) Blanchard. Rugged, husky, and just turning forty-two, Butch Blanchard's career admirably fitted him for full understanding of the nature and urgency of the effort.

Pilot of the first B-29 into China in World War II, this West Pointer later was operations officer of the Twentieth Air Force in the Mariana Islands. In that capacity he wrote the operations order in 1945, for the dropping of the first atomic bomb on Hiroshima by the B-29 "Enola Gay" of the 509th Bombardment Wing. Later, as commanding officer of that wing, he returned to the Pacific to participate in the "Operation Crossroads" postwar atomic bomb testing at Bikini Atoll.

Understanding of the potential Communist enemy grew in the summer of 1956. At that time General Blanchard was in the select group that accompanied General Nathan Twining, then Air Force chief of staff, on an official visit to Russia, meeting military and political leaders, viewing the annual air show, and touring military points in the Moscow and Stalingrad areas.

Already in England nearly a year as commanding officer of the Strategic Air Command's Seventh Air Division, the atomic-armed striking force based there, Butch Blanchard needed no further indoctrination to press for an early agreement. The DEI success and the progress in Florida were merely added tools to build the confidence of the Air Ministry's Bomber Command that Thor would prove to be a reliable weapon system.

Lieutenant Colonel George Vanden Heuvel, then chief of the Systems Integration Division of the Thor program office at Ballistic Missile Division headquarters, received orders to go to London for a critical series of meetings in mid-January. His job: serve as BMD's technical advisor to General Blanchard's negotiating team.

Vanden Heuvel did some personal thinking before dashing off to London, however. Higher headquarters in the Air Force had given firm indication that everything looked favorable for a final agreement that would implement the general agreement between President Eisenhower and Prime Minister Macmillan at Bermuda, on the matter of American-supplied "guided missiles," nine months before. It appeared to him that a crash effort to deploy Thor to England was imminent. If this developed, no time could be spared rounding up the needed civilian technical people on the scene there to get the ball rolling.

With this in mind, he arranged for a high-level team from Space Technology Laboratories and for the associate contractors, Douglas, General Electric, and AC Spark Plug, to arrive in London on January 26, by which date it seemed the agreement would be completed.

Vanden Heuvel's foresight before leaving for England was

well founded. Events moved even faster than he had guessed. The broad agreement was completed by January 20. Defense Secretary McElroy suddenly moved up the date for deployment of the first fifteen-missile squadron to England, with limited operational capability, from July of the following year to the July 1–December 31 period of 1958.

Certain factors were clear enough in the still-secret agreement: United Kingdom forces would man the missiles, and these RAF troops would be trained in the United States at American expense. But the United Kingdom would have to provide the sites and construct the bases at its own expense, perform the "brick-and-mortar" work, while the United States Air Force would retain custody and control of the nuclear warheads "in accordance with United States law."

These, however, were matters chiefly of human relationships. The really plaguing problems suddenly thrust upon all concerned were those of physical limitations in meeting the deadlines.

At this instant they were charged with constructing combat launching sites, an ultimate total of sixty launchers at points scattered over the countryside at sites not yet selected finally, built to engineering tolerances beyond all normal standards. Yet the first such site at Vandenberg Air Force Base as a prototype had not yet been built, nor was a combat Thor destined to be launched there until December 16, 1958, just two weeks before the initial "operational in England" deadline!

With the nucleus of the contractor teams on hand, the USAF and RAF pushed forward in many directions, but still in utmost secrecy, under the British-selected code name of "Project Emily." This soon was compromised and another name substituted. But to the more than one thousand Americans eventually involved in the task there, it always would remain "Emily," whether they loved her or hated her at the moment.

One of the first tasks was site selection. For reasons of economy paralleling similar solutions by our own military, the RAF elected to build all facilities on government-owned land, and England, in wartime a green checkerboard of airfields, had many sites available.

Anticipating that agreement would be reached, the sites already had been winnowed down to the most suitable. One consideration, for instance, specified that each squadron would have its headquarters at an "existing permanent" base. This assured sufficient housing without building anew, and a hangar of forty-five thousand square feet floor space that could be converted into a RIM (reception-inspection-maintenance) building for the squadron's fifteen missiles. One launching complex of three pads also would be there. And each squadron headquarters site would be so chosen that the other four launching complexes, of three missiles each, could be spotted on disused satellite airstrips within the necessary twenty- to thirty-mile dispersion distance.

(With similar anticipation in late 1957, BMD realized that the transporter-erectors already under construction at Food Machinery and Chemical Corporation in Northern California, with fixed rear axles, never would be able to negotiate the rural roads of England between an airhead and the actual launching sites. A change was ordered to make the rear ends steerable, in hook-and-ladder fire-truck style. By February of 1958, the first of these was being road-tested in secrecy on perimeter roads of Moffett Naval Air Station on San Francisco Bay, through co-operation of the United States Navy. Nor were the fixed rear-end versions, of which only three were built, chalked up as a loss. They have served long and useful careers at Canaveral.)

It still was necessary, however, for the American teams, military and contractor, to participate in final site selection. In Colonel Vanden Heuvel's words, this was "strictly cloak and dagger." The Conservative government of Britain was not ready to disclose the program in great detail, correctly expecting concern about the nuclear warheads among the rural populace and an uproar from the small but vocal pacifist segment. Moreover, in fact, the full and formal agreement between the United States and the United Kingdom had not been spelled out at the diplomatic level.

Hence the trips to the countryside, at this period, were made in RAF vehicles, with American officers in civilian clothes. It was strictly understood that, off the RAF bases, the British would do all the talking; no one with an American accent was to speak up for anything. And even on the RAF bases, the Americans, military and civilian alike, were introduced as a "Strategic Air Command team concerned with their (bomber) reflex program." Any discussions of transportation problems to bring in concrete, or availability of labor, were explained away as having to do with programs for parking areas for aircraft.

The British Ministry of Transport and the affected local County Councils surveyed the roads between proposed main bases and satellite launching areas on similar pretexts to find where, as the British termed it, work would be necessary "to ease the bends."

In this fashion, vital problems of future land movements were solved. The most accessible sites were selected. The big USAF-SAC base at Lakenheath was chosen as the centrally situated airhead for the tons upon tons of matériel soon to be arriving from the United States. And the 1917-vintage permanent base at RAF Feltwell was picked as the headquarters of the RAF Bomber Command's first missile squadron.

"Easing the bends" was but the least of the language problem. Even though many of the Americans had served in England in World War II, the scope of the engineering problem facing them brought the realization of entirely new communications barriers between peoples normally felt to share a common language.

Differences in engineering terminology and the practical language of construction workers between the two groups were as widely at variance as normal electrical power supplies in America and England. The "transformer" in the language area had to be groups of people, working together in good humor, as the exacting criteria for Thor base construction were translated into matters of mutual understanding.

The first drawings of basic requirements were supplied early in February. Through the face-to-face method of working out the problems, the full set of more than three hundred working drawings for the first complex had been prepared and translated from American into English by April 21.

Before the full job would be completed, the four squadrons would require excavating 600,000 cubic yards of earth, filling in another 400,000 cubic yards, and pouring 235,000 yards of concrete, in just the founding of the missile launching sites, plus driving 490 deep piles to prevent settlement from almost absolute "true" in the marshy, reclaimed land areas.

These exacting demands had a firm basis. No missile can reach its target on a ballistic course unless the gyroscopes of its guidance system "know" precisely where it starts its flight.

This called for astrogeodetic surveys both within and outside each launching site. Here again, teamwork to speed the task and area assignments to maintain as much secrecy as possible were the solution. The Director of Military Surveys of the British War Office did the work outside the sites. Americans went to work on it inside the swiftly fenced areas in the RAF Feltwell complex.

With many wheels turning and seemingly meshing, the United Kingdom's Minister of Defense was ready to present to Parliament on February 22, 1958, the White Paper with the text of the agreement that would put American nuclear warheaded Thor ballistic missiles in England.

But he did not disclose their locations, their numbers, or their operational dates. For some time, the cloak of secrecy would continue to shield many details of the new dagger being aimed defensively at Russia.

20.

THE CALCULATED RISK

*The United States
Through May, 1958*

FROM the beginning of the year, it had been growingly apparent that Thor would be cast in many roles beyond that of deterring war in the post-U-2 period.

Two things happened in secrecy. One, already noted here, was institution of the Thor-Able program to test advanced nose-cone re-entry vehicles for the Atlas. The other was President Eisenhower's assignment of highest national "DX" ("crash") priority in February to Weapon System WS-117L, the advanced reconnaissance satellite program leading to the Samos "sky spy" and the Midas infrared-missile-launching detection system, which would have to be pioneered by the Thor-boosted polar-orbiting satellite test vehicle to be known as Discoverer.

General Schriever, in answer to congressional questions on January 9, had publicly forecast confidently that Thor "plus existing second and third stage hardware [can] perform unmanned reconnaissance of the moon at an early date." With the nation clamoring for space achievements, such a program was initiated openly in March under the Defense Department's Advanced Research Projects Administration (ARPA), with Thor again the first-stage "work horse" booster.

Defense Secretary McElroy announced the lunar-probes program on March 27, along with plans for certain other future space adventures. ARPA's Director Roy W. Johnson assigned three such missions to General Schriever's BMD. The officer reasserted his confidence that the growing Air Force missile arsenal could do the job.

Simultaneously, Vandenberg Air Force Base (still called Cooke AFB then) was transferred from the Ballistic Missile Division to the Strategic Air Command. Major General David Wade of SAC took command of the First Missile Division. "Blue suiter" Air Force men of his 392nd Missile Training Squadron already were receiving technical training on the Thor at the Douglas plant, at Rocketdyne, and elsewhere.

Douglas Aircraft, meanwhile, was setting up shop at their Tucson, Arizona, facilities, with a technical faculty of one hundred, to train the RAF missilemen for the first two squadrons in England and return them to the combat sites before there would be facilities ready for a "graduation" firing at Vandenberg. (Other RAF men would learn "on the job" in England as the launching complexes were built, then come to Vandenberg for actual firings. The first RAF men trained at Douglas-Tucson, back manning the first sites in the United Kingdom during the first actual RAF launchings in California, then would return to the United States for their chance at firing.)

During these same critical months, the Thor weapon system was still undergoing R & D testing at Canaveral, matching failures with successes in the unending quest for reliability that every one of its multiple purposes demanded.

And it was against this seemingly overwhelming burden of assignments that Thor's greatest problem, and General Schriever's toughest decision, arose. That was the turbopump problem.

Research and testing following discovery of a turbopump failure months before in a tied-down, routine engine test at Rocketdyne's Santa Susana test facilities already had resulted in some modifications. One was increasing the pressurization to correct what appeared to cause oil-frothing at high altitudes.

Rocketdyne was producing the Thor engines in what was termed the "block system." During the production of a certain number, or "block," of engines, all changes and modifications developed—usually for simplification and reduction of the number of parts—would be incorporated in the next production "block." The increased pressurization of the turbopump bearing casing had been introduced into the current "block" and there was no indication of further difficulties from this area.

(The Army, in its Jupiter IRBM program, had a different experience, losing two missiles late in 1957 due to turbopump "bearing-walking" problems. In March the Army missile chief, General John Medaris, elected to halt his testing program and refit all his Jupiter engines with redesigned turbopump systems.)

Here is how the Air Force Ballistic Missile Division moved forward to a similar moment of decision later in 1958, and why a different course was taken.

Flight testing at Canaveral in 1958 resumed on January 28. The Thor was missile number 114, still checking out the guidance phase. It lost stability in guidance and, after 152 seconds of flight, was destroyed by the range safety officer at Patrick AFB.

The next launching was Thor 120, first of the so-called "120 series."

Even at the distance to which they were restricted, newsmen saw that there was something different about Thor 120. The nose cone this time was little more than a button in shape. One reporter—Darrell Garwood, then of INS—called it a "coolie hat." As it thundered upward, leaving a Navy Vanguard and an Army Jupiter-C standing in pads on either side of it on February 28, he also described it tentatively but correctly as "the first American space rocket fully equipped to carry a hydrogen bomb warhead."

The "coolie hat" was the first of the General Electric copper heat-sink nose cones to be tested (on Thors numbered 120 and on sequentially). And the first test was successful.

It was a different story, however, when Thor 121 was ignited on April 19 in the next launching attempt. It crashed on the pad. But there was some satisfaction even in that. GE engineers, retrieving the copper shield as soon as they could after its plunge down into the flaming metal of the engine and the steel and concrete of the launching pad, discovered jubilantly that it had been so little damaged it actually could have been refurbished and used again.

Four days later another, still differently configured Thor stood ready. Its launching this April 23, 1958, was historic in many aspects. On its side was the number 116. On its top arose a slender, mushroom-capped extension. This was the first Thor-Able, one of three Thors—116, 118, and 119—pulled out of the production line for modification and mating to the Able second stage, built by STL and powered by the Aerojet-General engine of the Vanguard second stage.

Its goal: carry and test an advanced re-entry vehicle for the Atlas ICBM the full ICBM range of more than six thousand statute miles, at ICBM speeds of more than 17,250 miles an hour, nine months before the Atlas itself would be ready for a full-range flight, to make sure that it could withstand the blast-furnace heat of coming back into the atmosphere from six hundred to eight hundred miles up.

Thor 116-Able had two secrets in the payload compartment just behind the heat shield of the re-entry vehicle.

One, not disclosed for several days afterward, was a special compartment contrived at STL and containing a live mouse, to test biomedical reaction to g forces and weightlessness.

The other, disclosed here for the first time, was a two-ounce shot glass of Old Granddad bourbon, well sealed and overlabeled "Aged in Space." But it never went aloft. Someone tipped off Colonel Eichel from BMD during the countdown and it was promptly removed.

But it mattered little. Thor 116's propulsion system failed after 146 seconds of powered flight. The telemetry told the story: turbopump gearbox failure.

BMD, STL, and Rocketdyne plunged back into the records of all other launchings for comparison of telemetric reports. It was then that the fine tracings from the shorter-than-planned flight of 108 the previous October, so nearly perfect in burning time that it had gone unnoticed, was pinned down as probable gearbox failure.

The question was posed within the Thor program at once: should the Air Force suspend all testing until the eight Thors then either ready or nearly ready for a variety of important launchings—two more Thor-Ables, the first combat-configured Thor, two others to test the Bell Laboratories guidance system in support of the Titan ICBM program, perhaps the moon itself—had been refitted?

Answering the question was even more difficult than the dictates of military urgency, engineering abilities, scientific interests, and politico-public reaction obviously imposed. Added to it at the moment was a matter of personal grief and professional loss beyond the matter of Thor and the gearbox.

On April 21, just two days before Thor 116 failed, a United Air Lines DC-7 bound east from Los Angeles and an Air Force F-100-F out of Nellis AFB collided at twenty-one thousand feet near Las Vegas's famous gambling strip in Nevada.

The location, ironically, was above Potosi Mountain, where Actress Carole Lombard had died in a plane crash in 1942.

This time all forty-seven aboard the airliner and the two officers aboard the jet perished, after each pilot had just enough time to cry out "Mayday!" on the radio.

Among the casualties, press reports identified John Barrett Emanuel of Douglas, William H. Torrans of STL, and Robert

J. Hight, treasurer of STL's parent company, Ramo-Wool-dridge. There has been no public identification of assignment until now, however, other than rank and home addresses, of three Air Force officers on the airliner.

Actually en route to SAC at Omaha, they were Major Lyndell Highley, Major Robert Darmody, and Captain Steve Paris. Major Highley was commanding officer, and the others key officers, of the 6592nd Support Squadron. Their motto was "In Thrust We Trust." Their assignment: targeting of ballistic missiles.

Widely known both at BMD and STL, where they were being trained in targeting procedures, their loss and that of the civilians could only add to the generally dismal immediate outlook.

The question "Continue or Suspend?" generated numerous conferences. Every aspect was considered by STL's Louis Dunn, Rube Mettler, Al Donovan, Adolph Thiel, Rocketdyne's Sam Hoffman and Tom Dixon, BMD's General Schriever, (then) Colonel Terhune, and Colonel Jacobson.

Mettler expressed a general view in saying, "Politically, it's absolute dynamite to lose a missile at this time. Each one lost means at least two trips to Washington for key BMD and STL people. The Army would make hay and the public would not understand."

He shared equally, however, another and opposite viewpoint from the standpoint of the basic defense program, put by another of the group into these words, "The primary matter is getting reliable missiles to England. Even if one of these blows after ninety seconds, we'd get a lot of the data we need from it. Should we do nothing, just go down a blind alley for three or four months because we know we have a marginal turbopump design in the test missiles?"

Dolph Thiel noted that the turbopump area already had been pinpointed, months before, as a marginal design with possibly several factors involved, and the redesigned system there would be incorporated in the downstream "block" of engines. "If we can get a final fix on the guidance system in June instead of October," he said, "and get some nose-cone flights out in June and July instead of September and October, we are well ahead even if it costs us one or two of these birds."

The actual record had been fourteen launchings with only two losses due to the turbopump. It came down to one thing: "We'll know every time we push the button, that there's one chance in seven it will fail."

Another declared, "That means we have six chances in seven it won't."

Only one man could make the decision, however. That was Bennie Schriever. Long after, an associate chuckled, "Bennie decided to take a chance of a public-relations licking and gain technically." The general's decision was, "Continue testing."

That "one in seven" already was waiting for him, in the booster engine of a particular launching that would be the most heartbreaking of the group in question. But the free world's first ballistic missile deterrent force in England was fully ready before the critical Summit days of 1960, not two months after, because of his willingness to "take a chance of a public-relations licking."

21.

EMILY—PART ONE

England
March to December, 1958

NIKITA KHRUSHCHEV became premier of all the Russias on March 27, 1958. Some thirty months later, he astounded the world by slipping off a shoe in the august, polished hall of the General Assembly of the United Nations and brandishing it menacingly. One of the major reasons this frenzied act could be considered one of frustration—for neither the shoe itself nor the figurative gantlet of conflict was hurled—already could be found in England when Khrushchev ascended to power: the swift organization of the American industrial and military team, along with RAF Bomber Command, to stake out the world's first ballistic missile fence against a potential aggressor.

In mid-March, Major Jamie Wallace headed up a team that flew to England with the mission of solving in advance as many problems as possible relative to the now definite

170

deployment of people, hundreds from the contractors, as well as the weapon system itself. Captain "Bucky" Walters was assigned to the latter problem.

When he arrived, the proximity of the first day of spring was not evident in the weather. It was raining, overcast, and gloomy. In the next six weeks, when it was not raining, there were snow flurries. Aside from the aspect of morale, it made physically more difficult Walter's primary task: to determine by actual test whether the huge transporter-erector could reach the tentatively selected sites.

The big vehicle, number four, the first with the rear-end steering, was flown out of Moffett Naval Air Station by a Military Air Transport Service C-124 in late March, as the first actual piece of Thor equipment sent to the United Kingdom. Before it was off-loaded on the glistening, rain-slick hard stand at Lakenheath, Bucky Walters had done a number of things.

After checking in with Lieutenant Colonel Vanden Heuvel's temporary headquarters at South Ruislip, a pleasant London suburb easily reached by the Underground (subway) from the city, Walters arranged his liaison through Seventh Air Division with the British organizations concerned. These included RAF Bomber Command, the Air Ministry, and the Ministry of Transport. Route surveys between Lakenheath and the various proposed sites were studied for the most serious bottlenecks. Then, with aircraft wheel chocks and fifty-gallon oil drums representing the major hazards, they were duplicated on secluded areas of Lakenheath's terrain.

United States Air Force troops were the first to start snaking the long, unwieldy transporter-erector through the automotive obstacle course. Once they had mastered it, using the Air Force "prime mover" M-52 truck tractor, they trained the RAF.

At this point an English-built truck tractor was substituted. Mating it with the transporter-erector was a problem in itself. It necessitated using a welding torch to hack away part of the rear-bumper arrangement of the tractor and rearranging a number of the lights on the cab. Simultaneously, the big clamshell claws that normally grasp the reclining missile's waist were removed. Other troops painted out all American insignia and gave the long trailer a new look of RAF blue over all. Both governments involved saw eye to eye on the reasons behind these changes. For one, there was no reason or desire to advertise at this early date where specific missile launching sites were to be located. For another, there was no desire even to emphasize the fact that the strange vehicle had anything to do with missiles. And there was a desire to emphasize the United Kingdom's role, even through paint and markings, in any major project. In other words, make it as difficult as possible for the Russians to determine what was going on, and do nothing to aggravate the anticipated disturbances by pacifist elements, the "ban the bomb" people, at construction sites.

The RAF readily picked up the knack of handling the equipment, and soon the first excursions outside Lakenheath Air Base began. Two Americans were in the cab of the prime mover on these exploratory runs to the various sites. They were Captain Bucky Walters and Douglas Aircraft's Ed Arthur. And neither is likely to forget the panoply of the travels, rivaling in a minor way the traditional changing of the guard at Buckingham Palace.

Each journey was under full escort, by representatives of the ministries concerned, the RAF, and the local constabulary. Each also crossed numerous lines of political jurisdiction. Under the British system of vesting considerable authority in local subdivisions, there was a miniature changing of the guard by escorting police constables as one community was left and another entered. And, quite obviously, the alert rural populace soon added basic sums until an American officer, in civilian garb, standing quietly on a station platform waiting for a London-bound train, quite often would be asked by another waiting passenger, "You're one of those missile people, aren't you?"

The unprecedented nature of the deployment plumped big problems of living accommodations into the lap of the United States Air Force. Normally in a weapons turnover to an allied nation, our own military already is thoroughly versed in its installation and operation, and merely transfers this knowledge to the second nation's forces. But the USAF had no troops trained in the new weaponry of ballistic missiles. It was as new to them as to the British. Hence, it had to be up to the contractors. That, in turn, meant there would be hundreds of their people in England, performing initially the tasks of installation, checkout, and education normally carried out on home soil.

Major (now Lieutenant Colonel) Sam Wilson representing the contracting and procurement arm, Ballistic Missile Center of Air Matériel Command, wrestled with that one.

Everything was educated guesswork at the start, and the best guess called for handling an influx of five hundred civilians.

Working from Inglewood, Wilson was in close contact with the first Douglas and Rocketdyne advance scouts who had gone to England and returned with their estimates of the problem. Selection of Lakenheath USAFB as the airhead, and of RAF Feltwell as the first squadron site to go into construction, was influenced heavily by the question of accommodations. The areas of the other three squadrons would have no USAF-controlled housing close enough to be of use, but Lakenheath at least could provide quarters for the civilian bachelors.

An early proposal was to lease passenger ships and turn them into anchored hotels for the work force and their families. The most central location possible, however, while well up a coastal river, still would have left transportation problems overland to the sites of eighty to one hundred miles daily. It was discarded.

Some of those going to England, of course, could and by choice would live in the towns near the sites, renting or leasing. But available accommodations "on the economy" would take care of only a relative few. Another portion would find temporary homes in hotels from Cambridge to Norwich.

One other stop-gap solution remained. That was in the use of unoccupied mansions of the countryside. To meet the initial influx, leases were taken on such mansions as Lynford Hall, Northcourt Guest House, and Brandon Parks Great House. Here many would find the facilities a bit ancient, but compensated for by spacious formal gardens and the ivied surroundings of a storied past.

The final answer for the future was trailers, but this solution in itself presented new issues. The British counterparts, called "caravans" or just "vans," are Spartan vehicles designed for holidays, not full-time living, and lack the facilities for year-round habitation. Moreover, the idea of "trailer cities" does not entirely appeal to the British mind. These factors resulted in simultaneous negotiations. One resulted in British firms being engaged by Douglas, with USAF funds, to build a fleet of trailers to Douglas' American-oriented specifications. The other was American agreement to keep them on the airfields and as much out of sight as possible.

In the end, happily, the villagers heard from their tradesmen the marvels of these American "caravans" and flocked to open-house events to see the amazing array of conveniences they contained, from refrigerators to washing machines. But that was many months down the road.

What would be the legal status of these contractor personnel? That was another puzzling question, for they were neither fish nor fowl under existing agreements. The so-called Status of Forces agreement made clear definition for members of the armed forces, and for technical representatives of civilian companies working with the armed forces overseas. But the hundreds soon heading for England did not come under either category.

Here again a mutual attitude of common sense, rather than of letter-perfect formality, provided the solution. What if a sports-car-happy American was involved in a traffic violation or an accident? Let him be tried under the English law the same as their own citizens, without argument. "Their court system is the same as ours," reasoned Wilson, "and I know they'll bend over backwards." It proved true.

In general, each question of legal status was taken up individually under a delicate gentleman's agreement carried out with skill and diplomacy. "This time it's yours, this time it's ours," was the tenor. All pressures to formalize the relationships, by agencies of either government pushing for hard-and-fast rules, were firmly resisted.

Events were marching forward on other fronts. On May 12, 1958, the first "prime contract" with an English construction firm was completed for the RAF Feltwell squadron. Many Douglas personnel already were on hand, at the moment working out of the firm's headquarters in a modern office building at 197 Knightsbridge in London's fashionable West End. The company programed its own airlift for Douglas personnel, a weekly charter flight by Pan American World Airways. On July 24, 1958, at 11:30 A.M., the first of these DC-7 transports greased onto the runway at Lakenheath. The sun, stranger though it was for the preceding months, turned on brilliantly to match the warmth of the welcome from Douglas people of the advance party.

Within the structure of the Seventh Air Division the USAF organization for Thor deployment was shaping up. General Blanchard's organization expanded to include a new assistant for ballistic missiles, actually to perform as "chairman" in co-ordinating American contractors, the USAF units concerned, and the RAF units assigned to the project.

Colonel George C. McDowell, fresh from the Industrial College of the Armed Forces, took over that key slot. Destined to be a delicate administrative post, providing the balance wheel between "voting" American elements and "non-voting," sometimes understandably critical British elements at regular meetings, it called for the type of background McDowell had.

A Detroit, Texas, native, then forty-five years old, he had a bachelor of arts degree from Arlington (Texas) State College before he entered West Point. There he earned a bachelor of science degree as well as his commission; later at the Harvard Graduate School of Business Administration he took his master's degree. For a period of six years before the assignment in England, the colonel had sponsored the development and initial installation of electronic data-processing equipment for business-type problems at Headquarters, USAF, and in AMC. Less glamorous, perhaps, than the talents required for piloting a jet interceptor, these abilities are recognized as equally vital in implementing the Air Force mission, and explain why Colonel McDowell already had been twice awarded both the Legion of Merit and the Commendation Ribbon.

Any such administrative job requires a counterpart in the field, a knowing straw boss to see that decisions are translated into action, whether by means of cajolery or sternness. This fell to Major (now Lieutenant Colonel) Frederic D. (Don) Selbie, Jr. A native New Yorker, Princeton University graduate, and pilot on twenty-three B-29 combat missions in the Pacific Theater in World War II, which earned him the Distinguished Flying Cross, the Air Medal with two oak leaf clusters, and the Commendation Medal, Don Selbie came to England in June, 1958, with his wife and four children, to take up his tasks as Maintenance Missile Staff Officer.

Still another organization under Seventh Air Division was the new 672nd Technical Training Squadron, created to perform the maintenance functions for the first RAF squadron until it could teach the British, and to continue indefinitely the custody of the nuclear warheads. Commanding the 672nd, which first had to teach itself how to perform those functions, was Colonel William A. Delehay, another Texan, whose World War II career took him to the China-Burma-India Theater and saw him return with the Distinguished Flying Cross with oak leaf cluster, Air Medal with oak leaf cluster, and the Legion of Merit.

The RAF, meanwhile, was putting together the personnel of its new missile structure as rapidly and as carefully as the USAF-SAC, plus overtones strictly British. In the words of an Air Ministry spokesman who reflected on the immense significance of the warhead involved and the unique chain of command over it: "Not since the days of Nelson will commanders be so directly linked with the Prime Minister in the implementation of the Government's foreign policy. We must have the very highest character."

The qualities were punched out for the card selection system—above-average technical education, demonstrated leadership, many other qualities—and the personnel files run through. From those whose cards were kicked out automatically, final selections for the first groups were made. Many suffered unexpected peacetime hardships, being rushed off from their families to the United States or to the construction sites without the normal British six months' notice of change of station. But each was indoctrinated with his role in the United Kingdom's, and in the free world's, ballistic missile spearhead of deterrent force. And each was enthusiastic for his part in the new era.

From all these outward signs it would seem that things were going along famously. The fact is, they were not.

While the dirt was flying by mid-May at Feltwell, the exacting specifications forced some of the concrete to be chipped away and repoured later, for example.

Where the British originally labeled the deployment "Operation Emily," BMD-BMC called it "Operation Go Away." Some of the cargo labeled with the latter title, flown to England, did not get delivered promptly because no one there knew the titles were synonymous.

Communications between the construction area in East Anglia and the Douglas plant in Santa Monica were sketchy and unreliable at first.

With the first combat-configured sites under simultaneous construction at Vandenberg and Sacramento, California, as well as RAF Feltwell, indications of necessary changes were cropping up at all three locations. The funneling of this information through Douglas and BMD, and the return relay of top-level decisions in all three directions, were time-consuming.

Word reached England early on July 31 of a tragic accident at the Sacramento facilities the previous day that would delay that location's ability to contribute to the program—

other than by grim, renewed warning that liquid oxygen is tricky stuff. During one of the initial "wet flow" tests of the ground-support equipment at the static, combat-configured facilities in Northern California, a lox line ruptured. The super-chilled liquid that had been collecting frost on the outside of the lines instantly turned into a flaming torch. Six men were badly burned. Jack Goodman, Douglas operations manager, rushed them to the hospital at Mather Air Force Base nearby. But three of them—Oscar Udager, Walter J. Milan, and John May—died in the days following. . . .

The "ban the bomb" demonstrators were becoming more active as months wore on. The opposition in Parliament became more critical as R & D launchings of Thor from Florida sometimes seemed less than unqualified successes, and echoes of our own Congressional inquiries reached London. Even in the generally equable Seventh Air Division-RAF meetings, the touchy situation would be reflected in a British voice inquiring whether or not they were being given "junk."

Despite the wholehearted efforts of both American Air Force and RAF personnel on the scene, plunging into the effort to the extent that they were working shoulder to shoulder with British civilian construction workers in the field virtually as laborers rather than technicians-in-training, it was becoming apparent that the program was "slipping." The first squadron plainly would not be operational in the strictly military sense by December 31, 1958. In the beginning that was a "target" date rather than a fixed schedule. As happened so often, however, like rumors enlarging as they are spread, it eventually became regarded by those outside the Thor program as a pledge. Conversely, those within the program found themselves under extreme pressure to deliver something they had not promised. It was September 1, in fact, before the "brick and mortar" work for the first launching complex at RAF Feltwell could be turned over to GSE installation, checkout, and acceptance. Still to be installed for that first squadron were four more complexes of three missiles each, and the suddenly sacrosanct "due date" was but four months away.

Colonel Jacobson, back at Inglewood headquarters, was aware of the situation in England. He also believed firmly that no communications system in the world can replace direct observation in finding out what is wrong in a given situation. And it again had been a hot summer of discontent and violence in the world, taking nothing away from the urgency of putting Thor in business as a deterrent.

It had started in June, with Communist announcement of the execution of former Hungarian Premier Imre Nagy in brazen retaliation for the ill-fated freedom revolt of 1956. On July 14, Arab nationalists seized the Iraqi government and assassinated King Faisal II. The following day, President Eisenhower rushed United States Marines to Lebanon, at that government's request, to forestall a threatened attempt by Russia and the United Arab Republic to overthrow the Lebanese government. And toward the end of August, the Chinese Communists unleashed their torrential shelling of the Nationalist-held Quemoy Island group.

Against such a backdrop, Colonel Jake decided on some direct action of his own.

Colonel Sid Green had just pleaded for two weeks' leave to "get away from it all" after seemingly endless months of intensive effort. Jake agreed. He thought an ocean trip would be fine. By air. Almost before he knew what was happening, Sid Green was on his way to England, and a few days later he was sending back a detailed report by cable.

As a result, Colonel Jake organized a BMD management team and hustled them off to England to see what was needed to recoup time losses and prevent future delays. It was a small group. It included Major Jamie Wallace, whose specialty was GSE, and Major Richard Randall, his counterpart for Thor's airborne systems. With them also were Colonel Charles Woodward, the SAC officer assigned to BMD-Thor at Inglewood, and a BMC representative. The team spent four days studying the problem in England. Colonel Jake and Jack Bromberg flew over to join them and hear their report.

Jamie Wallace made the report verbally. In some aspects it was too hot to put on paper. In essence, everybody concerned had underestimated the severity of the problems in this unique job as much as they had misjudged its true nature. There were not enough people in England to handle it, and in large degree they were, while fully qualified in their own domains, not the right people. The basic misconception, Wallace pointed out, was the original premise that deployment to England would be a production problem, when in reality it was basically an engineering problem. The crews in Florida conducting R & D launchings were engineers, not production people. And the combat launching site construction in England was just as much R & D as the launchings in Florida.

Colonel Jake said succinctly, "I sent you over to find out and I agree." He took it to General Schriever, and the contractors were called in for reorientation. But even this direct approach took time—too much time—to implement.

It was Thanksgiving Eve in East Anglia, but the RAF and USAF missilemen at Feltwell were not concerned with the American holiday or the traditional turkey on the table. They just hoped that Thor would not prove to be a turkey on the following day.

For that was the time set for the first raising of a Thor to its vertical launching position, on the first launching pad checked out for full test. It was fully realized any remaining secrecy about that site would be gone once the white tube was pushed erect by the transporter-erector. It would be visible for miles across the billiard-table flatness of the countryside. Hence, the British press had been invited for the occasion.

Colonel George C. McDowell, far away at Seventh Air Division headquarters, remembered that in his sleep during the night. It brought him instantly awake and bolt upright with the terrifying thought, "What if it doesn't work?"

Colonel McDowell grabbed a telephone and called Feltwell. What was the weather? Pea-soup fog? Great! With no one outside the base able to see anything going on within it due to the fog, he ordered them to try out the Thor's erector during the night, not just once, but three times. Right up to midnight of that damp, chill November night, they pushed the Thor up, brought it down, pushed it up again, just to be sure there would be no failure when the eyes of the press and the local populace were on it the next day.

Fortune, if not the weather, smiled on Thor that Thanksgiving Day. It performed perfectly and impressively for the visitors.

Behind the scenes, however, the Air Force and Douglas knew things were not as smooth as the demonstration indicated. Colonel McDowell sighed, "This is like assembling a DC-8 at the DeHavilland factory here and doing the engineering back in Santa Monica." For months, as the new year approached, there were nightly meetings, seven days a week, in the RIM building at Feltwell.

There was a big production control board on the wall. It showed the milestones they hoped to reach and how actual progress was lagging. "After the 5:30 roll call," Don Selbie would chuckle later in retrospect, "the name-calling contests began." Everyone had already put in a full day. But at this hour they sorted out the production problems of that particular day and the problems that had to be solved during the night before work could start the next day.

One common denominator stood out. It was a lack of trained manpower, the extremely small corps of people who truthfully could be called Thor technicians, to perform the complex work of installation and checkout of the maze of cables and connections comprising the nervous and circulatory systems that made Thor live. And there was no possibility at that moment of bringing in more people from the United States. All trailers delivered to date were in use. All available housing within a fifty-mile radius was taken up.

This was the breach filled in those months by 250 Air Force personnel and many of the RAF men, working in effect as Douglas employees. There were, admittedly, some quarters prone to snap, "This is illegal; you just can't do it." But, fortunately for the program and the free world, there were wiser heads who, in effect, retorted, "Perhaps. But there's a job to be done." And there was no loss in the effort. The troops of both nations, in the slightly different shades of blue uniforms, were getting the most effective on-the-job training that could be devised, helping build from the ground up the weapon system they would man.

Similarly, the Air Matériel Command had to "make do." It was charged with the vital role of quality control on the Thor installations, the same as it is at the end of any airplane production line, charged with critical approval before acceptance. Yet AMC had only one officer on the scene, and there was no room to bring more. While it never was approved officially, he dug around through the high-caliber personnel of the 672nd Technical Training Squadron and picked eight of the best technicians of the crop. He made them AMC quality-control men. "Without them," a ranking officer said later, "we never would have kept up with the schedule."

Colonel McDowell had still another time-gnawing problem on his hands, too. With the Thor deployment program more or less "in the open," fantastic numbers of people who could not be turned down—congressmen, senators, top-level representatives of Department of Defense and various Pentagon agencies—wanted to see what was going on.

For weeks during this period Colonel McDowell left his South Ruislip desk daily for the short drive to Northolt Airdome, boarded an Air Force C-47 for the forty-five-minute hop to Lakenheath, took another drive to Feltwell RAF, then backtracked at day's end. The purposes: to escort or accompany visiting VIPs many of the days and to check on one bottleneck or another on other days. Colonel Delehay's 672nd Squadron headquarters file soon was bulging with official photographs of arriving and departing dignitaries, none of whom realized that each was contributing a few minutes here, an hour there, to the total time lost in Thor's deployment.

These things, in total but not in specific detail, were realized back at BMD headquarters. There was a production control board there, too. The unreached milestones loomed graver at each "black Friday" session of the staff, usually presided over by General Schriever. Colonel Terhune and Colonel Jake had been commuting regularly to England, the latter ten times in the growingly critical situation. But even more direct action seemed indicated. And again it was Major Jamie Wallace who got the nod from Colonel Jake to fly to England, this time with the top Thor people at Douglas. They were Vice-President Leo Carter and the Thor program chief, Jack Bromberg.

Jamie had the highest respect for his traveling companions. He knew they needed no guidance in putting their fingers on the critical problems, and in coming up with solutions where such might seem improbable. When they climbed off the plane in London, he said: "Well, Jack, I know you and Leo want to snoop around a little, and I've got to pick up my contacts. Suppose I meet you three days from now up at Feltwell and see what we've found out?"

By the time they joined up at Feltwell, Carter and Bromberg had found enough problems to require hours of discussion. The solution was much different. Bromberg actually had had it in mind for some weeks. It amounted to two words: Bill Duval.

They headed back for the Douglas Knightsbridge office in London to place an overseas call to "Douglas House," the big mansion on the beach between Cape Canaveral and Patrick Air Force Base in Florida which the firm had leased as their headquarters.

22.

THE "ONE IN SEVEN"

Cape Canaveral, Florida
June 4 to August 17, 1958

BILL DUVAL, officially entitled the senior Douglas resident representative at the Cape Canaveral Field Station, and certain key personnel under him had been advised secretly of the lunar-probe plans months before General Schriever's momentous decision to continue testing despite the threat of trouble with the Thor's turbopump gearbox. The forthcoming shots to reconnoiter the vicinity of the moon, promised publicly in March, were to be called the Thor-Able-1 series. Those long "in the know" included Bill Stitt, Duval's capable technical assistant, and Ted Gordon, who would serve as test conductor in the blockhouse when it came time to reach out toward the earth's natural satellite. But the necessity for success was more pressing than ever. Since May 15, two weeks before, Russia's Sputnik III had been orbiting the earth. Even though America already had three satellites whirling about the earth—Explorers I and III and Vanguard I—in the first three months of 1958, the weight of the latest Soviet venture seemed to cancel them out in the public mind. Where America's three satellites totaled some 112 pounds, Sputnik III alone put an estimated seven thousand pounds in orbit.

To a public still groping for the meanings of space exploration, the Red satellite's size was more impressive, more spectacular, than Explorer I's discovery of the Van Allen radiation belts about the earth, rated as probably the most important discovery of the International Geophysical Year.

Project Thor-Able-1, however, was only another ball to juggle for the Thor launching teams melded of Air Force, Douglas, STL, and other contractor personnel at the Cape.

R & D of the Thor combat missile for the sites already under construction in England had to be pushed relentlessly. There were two more launchings slated in the so-called Project Thor-Able-0 series to test nose cones for the Atlas over the five-thousand-nautical-mile ICBM range against extreme velocities and temperatures. And still another task had been assigned to Thor, simply because it already was the most adaptable, most available work-horse ballistic missile in history, thanks to Bennie Schriever's concept of concurrency, the unflagging drive of all concerned to make it work, and Douglas' ability to swing into a production-line approach on the first day.

This added starter was testing of the Bell Telephone Laboratories' guidance system for the Titan ICBM, one more step down the road beyond Atlas and nowhere near readiness to flight-test any components at this date. That was the mission on June 4, 1958, of Thor 115, the first to be launched since the turbopump gearbox failure of 116 back on April 23, which brought the pause for decision.

Major Dick Randall and Colonel (then Lieutenant Colonel) Charles G. (Moose) Mathison were in the steel-doored blockhouse at lift-off.

It was what Randall called "one of those odd-ball" flights, by intent at first, by accident a few moments later.

The program called for simulation of wind shear, to determine how the guidance would react if the missile were to encounter violent winds pushing and tugging at it in changing directions at different altitudes as it climbed through the atmosphere. To duplicate such a situation, the test team was deliberately causing it to pitch violently, several degrees upward, then several degrees in a downward direction, during its powered flight. The pitching was so marked that observers outside the blockhouse, back on the roof of central control three miles away, could see it with the naked eye.

And suddenly they saw something else.

"Something's falling off the bird!" someone cried. The word quickly reached the blockhouse.

"Now what the hell could that be?" demanded Mathison, whose nickname, Moose, aptly fits his frame.

But there were no answers in the blindness of the blockhouse, where the closed-circuit television loses its view of the Thor when its exhaust flame clears the ground by a scant one hundred feet. The "picture" after that is painted by instruments and lights, at that moment, strangely enough, they were tracing out a perfect flight.

The instant the door at the rear could be opened, Moose and Randall barged through on a dead run for a waiting jeep.

Search crews already had been dispatched from central control. The pair from the blockhouse caught up with them in a nearby swamp just as they were retrieving the first piece from Thor 115. It was one of the fins, gleaming with factory newness in the late-afternoon sunshine. The amazed officers took it back to the blockhouse, where amazement turned to delight with the report that the mission had been flown with complete success.

That wayward fin, and another that had fallen off at the same time, forced a happy decision. For some time, engineers on the program had been debating whether the fins really were necessary. The tendency was, as a BMD officer put it, "to leave things alone where they are going good. But if it flies without them, take them off. They aren't much in weight, but obviously they're one piece of equipment we don't need."

Thors already built with fins, undergoing modification for space programs, were left with them. But the modification was cranked into the production line, and the fins were cranked out of the combat Thor configuration.

There was one more happy note about Thor 115. The wind-shear simulation, the loss of the fins, and then the total success of the flight convinced all hands of the structural integrity of the basic airframe. That item never again was a worry.

The team went back to minding its basic business on June 13, successfully launching Thor 122. This was another "Phase Three" shot, part of R & D for the IRBM weapon system for England, a further test of combined propulsion, guidance, and nose cone—everything in the combat version except for the simulated warhead and fuzing. It was an entirely satisfactory flight and left them eager for another in the growing list of "special" launchings.

This one was their second crack at the Thor-Able-0 series to test the ablated Atlas nose cone. The first had failed with the gearbox. Only three had been planned. Hence every effort at perfection in prelaunching checkout of this second try was exerted.

Again there was a tiny white mouse booked as a passenger. It was named Mia II, for "Mouse in Able" and in memory of Mia I, which perished in the April 23 failure. And this time the Air Force made no secret, at its prelaunching off-the-record briefing for the press, that the tiny rodent was in its STL-devised "mouse house" atop the rocket combination some ninety feet above the pad's flame buckets.

The ignition command for what was to be a historic flight, even though detailed results were withheld prudently at the time, came at 9:30 P.M. on July 9.

With its production number "119" standing out starkly from its white hull in the searchlights, the Thor boosted the Able upper stage, its instrumentation and transmitters, and Mia II, straight up toward the starry canopy above. After burnout of the Rocketdyne engine at 160 seconds, observers on the ground could see Thor break away with a farewell, final flash before the second-stage engine ignited and pushed ever upward on its arching flight toward the South Atlantic.

One-half hour later the nose-coned instrument package plunged back to the sea near Ascension Island, that slag pile of ancient volcanic eruptions that holds a British cable station and the far anchor of America's ICBM test range above water, one thousand miles off the West African coast.

The nose cone was parachuted automatically in the final phase of its fall. Two ships and two aircraft, cruising the fringes of the impact area, recorded it. But the area covered thousands of square miles. The dye marker in the nose cone, designed to stain the sea's surface, could not be found before darkness closed down the following day. The automatic radio signals from the package were sporadic and too weak to allow a firm fix. Aircraft swept the vast area again on the next day at low level, following the same precise patterns they would to seek and rescue a downed plane. But it was to no avail, and the search was called off.

There was firm reason for ending the quest. Even as the nose cone was engineered for buoyancy on impact with the water, it also was engineered to sink to the bottom after thirty-six hours. The ablated nose cone being tested represented almost countless tens of millions of dollars in research. It was top secret. If we could not find it, we certainly were not going to let it drift into the hands of potential enemies, already beginning to haunt sensitive sea areas with mysterious "trawlers."

In any case, telemetry had told the story. It was a bigger story than was disclosed publicly then.

It was obvious, of course, that the free world had successfully fired for the first time a ballistic vehicle that climbed to space, traveled to a target more than six thousand miles away, and managed to survive the blazing, abrading journey back into the atmosphere.

Mia II, as it was then announced, had been rocketed higher than any other living thing sent aloft before by the

United States. The high point of the trajectory was indicated as six hundred miles.

But there was more to be read in the tracings of the radioed "bits" of information. The apogee actually had been nearly one thousand miles above the earth. This took Mia II as far up in space as Russia's dog, Laika, had traveled at apogee aboard Sputnik II. The telemetry also disclosed that Mia II's career was even more historic. Whereas Laika had died in orbit and was cremated on Sputnik II's re-entry 162 days after the launching of the Russian satellite, Mia II survived the entire flight. There was full telemetric data on the mouse's heartbeat until impact, signifying that it was still living when it reached the sea. Mia II was the first living creature to visit space and return alive.

The significance of this, at such an early stage in space adventures, was apparent. "Getting a man up there is not the problem; it's getting him back," said one BMD officer with his mind on the problems of the years ahead.

The flight proved another point, if only on paper at the moment. The concept of adding a small third stage to the Thor-Able-0 had every capability of reaching the vicinity of the moon.

July, 1958, seemed to be a lucky month at Cape Canaveral. For the first time, everything seemed to be going better than could be hoped.

Bill Duval had added another team member at Douglas "House," one upon whom he would rely heavily in the future. He was A. E. (Sarge) Willer, who had been with Douglas since 1936, except for the United States Marine Corps service that gave him his nickname. Sarge knew the Thor well. He had been assistant superintendent of the Douglas Culver City Plant, the old "dog track," when Colonel Jake and Jamie Wallace staged their famous Christmas period design engineering inspection. Now he was assigned as works superintendent at the Florida facilities.

On July 12, Thor 123 was launched, still another in the Phase Three program toward the fully operational version for the United Kingdom. It was fully successful.

Eleven days later the crew sent up the third and final rocket of the Thor-Able-0 series, the last of the nose-cone tests for Atlas. Once again there was a mouse aboard. This time the press refused to call it Mia III. Instead, they dubbed it "Wickie," honoring a girl journalist of the area who had been faithful to the project throughout. Unfortunately there was no nose-cone recovery on that last Thor-Able-0, and "Wickie" joined her predecessors. But few mourned.

Recovery of the nose cone and the mouse would have been a real bonus, and planes were kept on the search through the second day. General Yates, the test center commander, made it clear that this was no failure. "We can answer most of the questions when we get the results of telemetry. We will be awfully close to what we want."

In fact, after the third Thor-Able-0 shot, there was a lot of talk about a new subject, "Thoric." This was the proposal that an upper stage on Thor could make it an ICBM as well as an IRBM. The name came from adding "ic" for "intercontinental" to the basic word "Thor." But Atlas, the "one-and-one-half stage" ICBM, was well along, and Titan, the first true two-stage ICBM, would be ready for its first test launching in December.

Moreover, the Thor-Able-0 flights had proved the point in hand. The ablated nose cones were successful. They could absorb the ICBM re-entry heat—so intense the boundary layers of the atmosphere about it decomposed into their elements and those, in turn, became gases—literally by melting away the laminated layers of its own surface. These flights confirmed the theory in the design of the nose cone that it could handle four times the rate of heat transfer generated in Thor's normal flight trajectory. The tests allowed a firm decision that General Electric's ablated re-entry vehicle could be incorporated in the first fully operational Atlas squadron without endangering performance or schedule.

So high was the confidence in Thor to do any job asked of it, during that month of July, 1958, that the Air Force began organizing and training a specialized squadron of C-119 "flying boxcars" for the most unique job in aviation. Their task was to learn how to catch in midair a parachuting capsule being returned by rocket from a satellite in orbit. That was a critical part of the Discoverer program still ahead for Thor.

No one was unduly concerned on July 26 when another routine Thor R & D launching of the Phase Three series failed after fifty-nine seconds of powered flight. The trouble was quickly traced to a lox valve. The flight was written down as "partially successful" and this was true; a great deal of valuable telemetric data had been recorded before the valve trouble.

On August 6, any flagging confidence was shored up again. Thor 117 performed well against another "odd-ball" pattern simulating vicious wind-shears in its powered flight.

No one could be blamed for having their eyes and interest through all those weeks centered chiefly on the launching set for 7:14 A.M., Sunday, August 17, 1958. This was the first of the long-planned Thor-Able-1 series.

It was history's first shot for the moon.

How strange could it be? The Air Force BMD and Douglas had not yet been able to complete testing of a Thor IRBM that could fly with accuracy from the United Kingdom to behind the Iron Curtain, over distances ranging from three hundred nautical miles minimum to fifteen hundred nautical miles maximum. Yet at a specific moment on a specific date, chosen for the ideal proximity and direction of the moon, this Thor was to boost into space a vehicle that would travel 240,000 miles, lead the moon like a hunter leading a duck, and rendezvous with it two and one-half days later.

Months before, however, astrophysicists had patted their obedient computers and declared that it could be done.

Far ahead, many people had been dispatched to many locations on the globe to track and control this fantastic vehicle. Some came from the Thor-Able-0 program. Lieutenant Colonel Donald R. Latham was at Jodrell Bank, site of the great British tracking installation with its giant 185-foot dish antenna near Manchester. Major John E. Richards, with Dr. George Mueller of STL, were in Singapore to co-ordinate the work of the station there. Polish-born Henry Samulson of STL had the critical spot at Hilo, Hawaii. If all went well, his would be the station "under" the lunar probe when the moment came to dispatch the signal to fire the retarding rocket, slowing it into a path about the moon. His would be the "golden key."

Weeks had been spent checking out and assembling the stack of rocket engines and the payload at Canaveral. Atop the modified Thor and its potential of 153,000 pounds of thrust in the Rocketdyne engine was the same second stage as in the Thor-Able-0 shots, the STL-built, Aerojet-powered engine of 7,500 pounds thrust. Crowning all was the spacecraft, thirty inches long, twenty-nine inches in diameter at midsection, and containing a Thiokol Chemical solid-propellant rocket to inject the package into its final flight path when the vicinity of the moon had been reached.

In that small package was a complex payload: a facsimile television to scan the moon; instruments to record magnetic fields, temperatures, and micrometeorite collisions; batteries; and two transmitters.

Months of study had gone into the unusual "reverse countdown." With the basic Thor, a launching time was planned. If bugs developed, the launching time simply "slipped" until they could be worked out. Sometimes the missile left the pad twenty or more hours after the planned moment. But this could not be allowed with a moon launching. There were only a few minutes' leeway at the propitious times. Hence the countdown was planned to start unusually early and blank "no work" periods were scheduled. If nothing was wrong, the crew would just sit there until the scheduled times to resume the count, so that, as far as man could plan, it would come out even at 7:14 A.M., Sunday, August 17, 1958.

That crew, also, had been long designated.

Ted Gordon was the Douglas test conductor, assisted by Earle Wollam. Miles (Mike) Ross was the STL test director.

Major (then captain) Millard E. (Brandy) Griffith was the Air Force test controller. Joe Broadbent was the man actually to push the button at "Zero." And there were many more.

There were those, for instance, of greater rank and stature, who knew they could not even be in the blockhouse, who stood atop Central Control miles away, staring in the pre-dawn at the 88.1-foot-tall combination aimed at the moon and awaiting its takeoff. They included General Schriever, General Yates, and Roy Johnson, director of the sponsoring Advanced Research Projects Agency of the Department of Defense.

It was a near-classic countdown.

No really serious problems developed. There was a slight delay in the final phase. Only four minutes late—at 7:18 A.M. instead of 7:14 A.M.—Thor number 127 lighted up its boot-straps and started a package for the moon.

If you wait for water to boil, seventy-seven seconds is a long time. Much can happen in that period. It did in the blockhouse of Pad 17-A at Cape Canaveral. There was jubila-tion. There were the spontaneous cries of encouragement for the vehicle rising above it. There was a surge of elation on top of Central Control. Back at BMD headquarters in California, where it was still only a little after 4 A.M., the teletype room was jammed with people who spurned sleep for news.

And at seventy-seven seconds, somewhere fifty thousand feet or more above Cape Canaveral, the Thor blew up. Dolph Thiel of STL sat with his head in his hands and wept. Others wished they could. It seemed too swift and miserable an end to a project so faithfully supported that experts in surgical caps, gowns, masks, and gloves had mounted the tall gantry to sterilize the payload with ultraviolet lamps, so that the moon would not be contaminated with earthly germs should the orbit plan miss and the moon be impacted. That "failure" was anticipated; but not the one so close to earth that transpired. It was a job for the "undertakers."

These were the men of the ships under Louis Berger, with salvage divers aboard under Vernon Nealy. They went to sea and found the Thor where it had fallen, retrieved it, and shipped its broken carcass back to Rocketdyne.

The fault was found quickly: the turbopump gearbox. At the most critical of all moments the"one in seven" had turned up to collect on the odds.

23.

PIONEERING

Cape Canaveral, Florida
October to December, 1958

THE Thor pads were silent at the Cape for nearly two months after the failure of the first lunar probe. But the knowing crowds of Floridians began gathering along the beaches again the night of October 10. Hundreds of cars lined the roads. Campfires were built. The floodlights picked out another three-stage combination waiting for launching, with the number 130 on the side of the Thor booster. This was the second lunar probe. Inside the blockhouse, virtually the same team was present. Tensions, if anything, were greater than on the first effort back in August. And at 3:42 A.M., October 11, came the word: "Main stage lift-off normal!"

The 88.1-foot-tall combination moved above the slight ground fog, the Thor's blazing thrust literally burning it away, and climbed on toward the glittering heavens overhead.

"Programing normally," was the report moments later, as telemetry showed that Thor was pushing the upper stages on the necessary course, northeasterly this time, over the Atlantic toward its planned rendezvous with the moon.

Somewhere seventy-five miles above the surface of the sea, Thor 130 finished its vital task and fell away. In quick order, the second stage added its thrust and dropped off, and the third stage ignited. A cluster of eight small vernier rockets attached to the payload itself added their small but vital "push," intended to accelerate the surgically sanitary, seventy-five-pound spacecraft, carrying forty pounds of instruments, to the critical speed above twenty-five thousand miles an hour required to escape earth's gravity.

An official announcement christened the spacecraft "Pioneer I" and called it "the first man-made object known to escape the earth's gravitational field."

Unfortunately, the latter was premature. Telemetry already was reporting the clews, even though they could not be translated until some time later: the first-stage trajectory, even though Thor performed perfectly, was a trifle too high; "escape velocity" would not be reached.

That was the story. Colonel Jake and the Douglas people argued against it even before it was made public, defending the Thor's role. Eventually, they were proved right. Final analysis showed that Thor performed properly and it was the second stage that fired off at an angle, preventing the full journey to the moon.

There was no question, however, that "Pioneer I" had been named aptly. From tracking data, electronic computers at STL predicted the vehicle would reach a point nearly eighty thousand miles in space. The deepest penetration previously was the 2,463-mile apogee of America's Vanguard I. By evening (on the East Coast) of October 11, the earth had turned enough under Pioneer's outward-bound trajectory so that the stations in Hawaii and Singapore had picked it up; it then had "passed" the Vanguard and traveled 67,850 miles out, nearly thirty times as deep into space.

It already was clear that the package soon would start its long fall back to the atmosphere.

A decision was made by the relatively new National Aeronautics and Space Administration, which had taken over the scientific direction of the lunar probes from the military's Advanced Research Projects Agency, to fire Pioneer's retrorocket. This originally was intended to slow it near the moon, perhaps put it in orbit about the moon. Now NASA hoped only to change Pioneer's ballistic, one-trip "out and back" trajectory into a satellite trajectory. That would have put it in a vast elliptical orbit about the earth and prolonged its scientific reporting life.

Henry Samulson pushed the "golden button" many times at his station near Hilo. But nothing happened. Only later did study of the telemetric data reveal that the temperature inside the space craft had dropped so unexpectedly low that the batteries designed to ignite the retrorocket were too chilled to respond.

Forty-three hours, seventeen and one-half minutes after being launched, Pioneer burned up during re-entry into the atmosphere in the Southwest Pacific near New Guinea.

But it was October 12, by then, Columbus Day. The Thor-boosted probe could take equal rank in exploration of the seas of space. Its final peak altitude, as corrected and verified later, was 70,700 miles. The meaning of that achievement was best characterized in a message to all who participated:

"This flight has truly pioneered in deep penetration into outer space ... it will yield knowledge of great benefit to mankind in adding to an understanding of the universe in which we live." Those were the words of President Eisenhower.

A memorable moment was approaching in Thor's military career as well. The next launching scheduled at the Cape was Thor 138, on November 5. This was the first "Emily-IOC" missile to be flown, the first "initial operational configuration" of Thor to be flight-tested of the design-frozen "birds" already being sent to England.

The launching, of course, was from an R & D pad. The only IOC training launching complex, with GSE duplicating that being built overseas, was still under construction at Vandenberg AFB in California.

To all intent, however, the missile itself was the same, with the exception of an instrumented "dummy" warhead.

And this made the results only the more disappointing. With certain key people of the RAF, plus USAF and civilian technical executives in England, fully aware of the configuration, Thor 138 was destroyed by the range safety officer after but thirty-five seconds of flight. A control malfunction was at fault.

Another heartbreak was in store for the team at Canaveral just three days later. The third and final Thor-Able-1, the last-chance shot of the series at the moon, was launched on November 8. Again the Thor did its part, adding another

mark in its own success column. But the Pioneer II's third
stage did not ignite. The payload fell back after reaching
an altitude of only 963 miles. In their increasingly dual life,
switching between scientific launchings and military R & D
launchings, the BMD and Douglas personnel turned again
to Thor's original deterrent role.

Throughout the balance of the year, Thor's role at Canaveral was strictly military. Launchings became almost a
weekly affair. And in these there now was "warhead information."

Starting with the November 26 launching of Thor 140, the
deadweight dummy in the nose cones of the Phase Three
R & D missiles was replaced with a special package from the
AEC's Sandia Corporation which put the project in the final
Phase Four testing. This package has the same center of
gravity, size, weight, and operating principles as the actual
nuclear warhead. It telemetrically reports on the functioning
of the arming devices and other items necessary to the "real
thing." But it has, of course, no radioactive materials, or even
conventional explosives, aboard.

Thor 140, opening a concentrated launching period which
saw ups and downs, but gradually more "ups" than "downs,"
was mainly successful. It traveled the required distance into
the general "broad ocean" target area still being used.

Thors 145 and 146 arrowed down the range on December
5 and December 16 respectively, each marching in closer to
the imaginary bull's-eye than its predecessor. Unhappily, the
year's effort there ended on a sour note. Thor 149, launched
December 30, developed a valve malfunction. Its flight was
erratic. The RSO pushed the destruct button after fifty-two
seconds of flight.

But Major Dick Randall could total up his score sheet, count twenty Thor launchings in the year, six of them for special purposes in the Thor-Able-0 and Thor-Able-1 programs, and declare: "We're getting our feet wet!"

Moreover, things were stirring on the West Coast. A new "shooting gallery" for Thor had just been baptized from the shore-line dunes at Vandenberg AFB.

24.

THE NEW "GALLERY"

Vandenberg AFB, California
December 16, 1958

DECEMBER 16, 1958, was scheduled as a vital date, an impressive milestone, in the history of Thor. It was planned to be the occasion of the first troop-launched IOC Thor, from the new, still incomplete troop-training facilities on the West Coast. If successful, it would go far to obviate the under-the-surface concern that had arisen at Thanksgiving in England about the weapon, supposedly to be operational in some degree by year's end, but never yet launched by GI personnel. It would help still the vocal opposition in the House of Commons.

Whether it would go or not, whether it would give a creditable, confidence-inspiring performance, was a question. On the basis of launchings from Cape Canaveral, it would be virtually a tossup. But the admitted risk had to be taken. The greatest possible attention had to be called to the event, and then the best had to be hoped for with crossed fingers. For such critical reasons, a build-up in the public-relations sense was conducted deliberately in the final month before the launching date.

Even this, however, had been preceded by a physical build-up rushed at the fastest pace possible.

In the realm of inevitable paperwork, ARDC had relinquished control of the First Missile Division on December 31, 1957. The following day, January 1, 1958, the Division and all subordinate units were assigned to Strategic Air Command control. And the day after that, Major General David Wade arrived at the still barren coastal site to take command.

He arrived on a scene of incredible daily changes, with aged Army barracks being refurbished into modern, sparkling quarters for the troops of the dawning aerospace age. Work was under way already on the first unit of 880 houses. Within a week of General Wade's arrival, another unit of 525 "Capehart" homes for anticipated military personnel was authorized. The citizens of the nearby communities, such as Lompoc and Santa Maria, were realizing that the missile age was there to stay, and it would loom large in their economy. On the main street of Santa Maria, cocktail lounges were now blossoming in neon grandeur, with appropriate names such as "The Countdown." Ed McCoy, the owner, and Mac Worden, the manager, at the venerable Santa Maria Inn, where Army troops and brass in two wars—World War II and Korea—had found homelike food and relaxation during the lively periods of Camp Cooke, suddenly found themselves handling a new type of trade, hearing a new language in the comfortable beamed-ceiling taproom.

Before the big fireplace evenings, terms like "thrust" and "guidance" replaced talk of "105s" and "right oblique."

They were spoken as much by civilians as by military men, for Camp Cooke previously had little need for engineers; those soldiers dealt with long-familiar weapons, not weapons that never yet had been tested operationally. And, as the Santa Maria Inn became unofficial press headquarters, there were periodic influxes of correspondents never seen in the days when close-order drill was the newsiest event of the hour.

The suddenly exciting tempo of the Inn's taproom, with its huge tables, broad fireplace, and leather-upholstered, straight-backed booths, kept Guy, the bespectacled, beaming chief bartender, busier than he had been in years. And he had plenty of use for Gin and Bourbon. Those, rather than drinks, were the names of his assistants—Ira Gin and Angel Bourbon. Ira, a World War II sailor, was of Chinese descent. Angel was the son of a Spanish mother and a French father.

And the excitement was contagious. Santa Maria sparked eventually from an initial apathy about the new program at "Cooke" to a literal "land-office boom" in land options, housing projects, and new motels and hotels. It was a frontier town on the new frontier of space.

Not even those living close by realized, however, just how unexplored the frontier remained.

All through the summer the construction gangs of the Vinnell Corporation, working under the Army Corps of Engineers and under patriotic no-strike pledges in understanding of the necessity, plugged away on the brick-and-mortar work for Thor as the British workmen of Sir Robert McAlpine and Sons were doing simultaneously at RAF Feltwell. Both were up against the same pioneering problems of building something unique in the world's history.

The United States Navy was equally busy, both at its long-established Naval Missile Facility at Point Mugu on the coast one hundred miles south, and at its sprawling new Point Arguello facilities immediately adjacent to and south of the Air Force lands across the Santa Ynez River. The Pacific Missile Range, commanded by Rear Admiral Jack P. Monroe, had the assignment of range safety and tracking, as the Air Force had at Patrick AFB and at Cape Canaveral in Florida. In many human aspects, the Navy's task of preparation was similar. The climate was drier and colder, but the fires kindled to clear the old artillery impact area, and the upward-jutting Tranquillon Peak, where a tracking station would be built, roiled up angry rattlesnakes the same as missile explosion fires did on the opposite coast. In addition, moreover, the Navy had the touchy job of going over the thousands of acres, inch by inch, to locate not alligators but, equally dangerous, "dud" shells from the Army's training for two conflicts.

"Concurrency" toward the December military launching attempt was being given one of its greatest workouts, as examination of certain dates will show.

The first "Emily-IOC" Thor missile arrived at the base's RIM building on August 13, but not by air. The only Army liaison plane runway had not yet been beefed up and lengthened to handle the C-124-type plane needed to transport a Thor. That first one came instead by truck, a twelve-hour journey over the 160 miles from Santa Monica, with a large share of the miles involving narrow, sharply winding coastal mountain roads.

The first detachment of thirty RAF troops arrived the following day from the Douglas school at Tucson, to become the first class taking the eight-week launching-site training at Vandenberg AFB (which officially would not even be named that in honor of the late General Hoyt S. Vandenberg, USAF Chief of Staff, until the following October 4).

These were not the first British missile troops to be trained in the United States. Many others before them had gone to school at the various plants concerned and returned to England without the opportunity actually to launch a missile. They would return later for that.

Nor did these RAF troops arriving in August directly get their hands on Thor 151. That bird basically belonged to the men of the 392nd Missile Training (Thor IRBM) Squadron of the First Missile Division's 704th Strategic Missile Wing, activated since September 15, 1957. These technicians had been in on-the-job factory training virtually ever since. Some of them had provided the keen manpower that helped make the big DEI at the Douglas plant, the Christmas before, the success that it was. Theirs was the honor, and the responsibility, of firing the first IOC Thor.

By this time, work was well enough along on the $6,200,000 construction program for the Thor complexes. It seemed sure that at least one launching pad and one "Emily-IOC" missile would be ready to go before the year's end. Consequently, General Wade made no secret of the arrivals, either of the Thor or of the RAF personnel. He publicly expressed the hope that they would have a graduation launching, although that was not in the cards.

The only Thor complex actually completed in the basic construction stage at Vandenberg in August was 75-1. Others, designed for the "special purpose" Discoverer launchings, were farther down the road, in preparation for Samos and Midas satellites. And GSE on this complex would not be finished until February, 1959.

Complex 75-2, consisting of three IOC training stands, would not see the end of "brick-and-mortar" work until December, with full GSE installation unfinished until the following April.

And the 75-1 complex, of two static captive firing stands, was destined for construction completion in November, and for GSE completion in March, 1959.

Hence, it was not until November 25, 1958, that Murray Snyder, Assistant Secretary of Defense for Public Affairs, flew out to Vandenberg AFB to meet with the press in the new base theater and put a date—"early next month"—on the baptismal launching of a long-range ballistic missile from the base.

That same month of November the indirect thunder of Thor was having repercussions elsewhere in California, even before its initial West Coast launching.

Long Beach Municipal Airport, adjoined by another big Douglas plant where giants such as the C-124 Globemaster and later the DC-8 jetliner were built, had become the shipping point for the airlift that reached to Lakenheath, the aerial beachhead in England.

Delivery flights of completed missiles, components, GSE equipment, and other items out of Long Beach had climbed to more than thirty a month. Local residents were up in arms over the noise factor resulting from the increased military traffic. General Ritland, General Schriever's vice-commander at BMD, took on that problem with a direct appeal for forbearance. He explained to a community conference called by the Air Force the airport's major role in the drive to achieve operational readiness of Thor in England.

The citizenry bowed to the urgency, but General Ritland's public appeal underscored the privately understood need to succeed at Vandenberg in December and to publicize the event.

To that end, there were 182 invited newsmen of press, radio, and television on hand at Vandenberg AFB on December 16. In addition, there was an almost equal number of dignitaries and guest observers packing the especially erected bleachers at the observation point inland from the surfside launching pad where Thor 151 waited recumbently for the swift "combat" countdown.

There were no mice aboard for this shot. But mice figured in the day. When reporters pulled the tarpaulin from the telephones on the picnic bench-worktable in the field, they found four pink little fingerling-sized baby mice huddled in a nest of weeds and seed fluff where they had been delivered by a warmth-seeking field mouse during the night.

Nor did anyone move to sweep them away. In contrast to the destructive potential of the Thor in the distance, they were gathered up and tended by the former German war bride who operated the catering truck at the site.

This was not the only contrast to the typical Florida scene

where all of America's previous ballistic missiles had been tested. There were unusual range safety problems here, too, which dictated in considerable degree when Thor 151 could be launched, even as vagrant shrimp boats could delay a Canaveral flight.

Almost directly alongside the pad ran the Southern Pacific Railroad tracks, over which Nikita Khrushchev eventually would ride through Vandenberg AFB en route from Los Angeles to San Francisco, only to stare pointedly seaward rather than acknowledge existence of the deterrent forces standing in the gantries that day. Scheduled passenger trains, such as the northbound and southbound "Daylights," could be anticipated. But not so with the freights, sometimes running more than one hundred cars long.

To meet this problem, low-flying aircraft kept a sharp lookout for approaching freight trains. Once one was spotted, a helicopter "escorted" it from one end of Vandenberg to the other, making sure no knight of the road—friendly or otherwise—decided to hop off within the base.

On launching day five such trains, plus technical considerations, delayed for more than three hours the planned initiation of the mock combat alert.

When it did come just past midafternoon, the sequence moved so rapidly that the spectators were left in almost breathless admiration. The first indication was a cry from someone, "She's coming up!"

The transporter-erector pushed Thor 151 erect and with equal precision removed itself back to a horizontal position. The launching crew, headed by Captain Bennie Castillo, proceeded with the fueling. To observers, the only clews were the white wisps of lox venting from the missile's tanks.

And it was just nineteen minutes from the launching order that flame lashed from the tail of the Thor and it started up. Professional decorum was lost at the observation point in spontaneous cheers.

In the two minutes before it went out of sight westward high over the Pacific Missile Range, the sixty-five-foot bullet climbed up past the declining sun, the bright diamond of its flame matching the color of the sun's own light, filtered by high cirrus clouds.

The launching "looked good," and telemetry confirmed it shortly afterward. It was classed "excellent" and the wires hummed with news of Thor's "firsts"—the first troop-launched, long-range, operational ballistic missile in the free world; the first from the new base where Atlas and Titan later would win the "operational" rank; and a day on which Thors were successfully launched from both coasts, for Number 146 had gone full range from the Cape earlier.

One of the guests, however, had additional thoughts. He was Senator Case of South Dakota. Realizing that there was no potential enemy within Thor's reach from California, while there were both usable bases and not inconsiderable doubts in the United Kingdom, he commented: "This should be reassuring to Great Britain that the weapon they are going to get works."

25.

EMILY—THE BAD WINTER

*United States and United Kingdom
Winter, 1958–59*

SELECTION of Bill Duval to take charge of the Thor's deployment in the United Kingdom was welcome news to Major Jamie Wallace. His verbal picture of Duval, on the surface a slender, rather short-statured man of mild appearance, told the reason: "He reminds you of the guys who punched oil lines through the desert, the kind that go in and don't let anything stop 'em. They just go ahead and do the job."

Duval himself was not so sure when he received the telephone call from London asking him to take on the task and make it move, and to meet a few days later in Dayton, Ohio, with Douglas Vice-President Leo Carter and Thor Director Jack Bromberg who were en route to Santa Monica from England. Primarily he was extremely surprised by the turn of events. Duval and his wife, Charlotte, a handsome and gracious woman better known as "Char," had learned to like the Cocoa Beach area about Cape Canaveral. Only two weeks before, Duval had confirmed with his direct superiors that he would be there for some time to come. They and their four children looked forward to the start of construction, just a week later, of a new home. To exchange suddenly those plans for the uncertainties of climate and companions in England, which they viewed then, in common with most Americans unfamiliar with the land, as austere and aloof, was a formidable prospect.

But there was an urgent job to be done, a challenge to be met. None knew this better than Bill Duval. He headed for the rendezvous in Dayton, leaving Char behind with more than a trace of understandable tears over all the shattered home-decorating plans so carefully made. It was, in a personal way, a blow such as the explosion of Thor 101 had been to the engineers and the Air Force nearly two years before.

That hurried flight to Ohio in early December, 1958, strangely presaged what Duval would find in England. He arrived at the Dayton hotel room to meet Carter and Bromberg fully as exhausted as they from traveling. He took off from Orlando and missed connections at Jacksonville due to an unusual Florida fog. From there he dog-legged north, thanks to two major airline strikes at the moment, continuing to miss, as he told them, "every airline connection known to man." And it was cold and snowing in Dayton.

There was not enough time at the conference to cram all the information into his aching head. The only solution was to spend a few days on the scene in England personally, determine his preliminary course of action there, then return to Florida to wind up affairs there.

One thing was certain, however. Leo Carter, as general manager of the Santa Monica Division of Douglas, was taking over-all general supervision of deployment from that end. Duval would be United Kingdom regional operations manager. And there would be no chain of command injected between them. Duval would report directly to Carter.

With that established, Duval hastened to London, Lakenheath, and Feltwell.

The date set by Defense Secretary McElroy to achieve some measure of combat readiness in England was December 31. It would be met, but only on a strictly emergency basis. Duval quickly learned that a missile could be gotten off from RAF Feltwell by year's end, but only if everyone's skills were pooled, including those of Douglas civilians. By that date, the British contractors would be able to complete the work on all fifteen launchers of the Feltwell complex, but only a fraction of the GSE, the complex systems, would be installed and checked out.

Five months earlier, the basic construction work had started at the second squadron ("complex" in British terminology) at RAF Hemswell, considerably to the north. While it would not be completed until the end of April, 1959, Douglas people already were needed there, spreading thinner the already inadequate forces. Moreover, the construction contract for the third Thor squadron of fifteen more launchers, at RAF Driffield, was due to be awarded before Christmas.

The schedules not only were slipping, Duval saw, but they

were bound to slip more unless drastic changes were made to transform the attitude from a factory-at-home approach to a remote-field-job approach. The team was not big enough and it was discouraged. They were working in snow and slush, but that was not the problem. Duval knew this from his experiences with field teams at White Sands, where they contended with the desert's reeling, scorching heat, and at Canaveral, where they cheerfully accepted exhausting hours in sweltering tropic heat. What was the answer? This was Duval's: "You work side by side with a man in a factory and, when the whistle blows, you don't see that man again until the whistle blows again the next day. But on projects like this, and this is true on any field project, people not only work together but they sleep, eat, and drink together.

"Particularly in a foreign country, people have more of a family tendency to pull themselves together in groups, and they have to get along together better. You can take the finest engineer, the finest technician, the finest inspector in the world; if he can't get along with people he's no good on a project like this."

That, Duval knew, was his job to correct through administrative changes, through obtaining the right people, looking over their off-hours activities to make them as livable as possible as well as channeling their work activities in the most efficient manner, and through recreation programs and the best housing arrangements possible.

And housing was due to get worse. Once the emphasis shifted from RAF Feltwell to RAF Hemswell, then on to Driffield and North Luffenham, the final squadron, they would be out of reach of the relative comforts of the USAF base at Lakenheath. That meant no more American-style

BOQs (Bachelor Officer Quarters) for the unmarried men, no access to USAF Officers' Clubs, no AFEX (Air Force Exchange) privileges at hand.

There was still another major problem: to jack up the morale and efficiency of the deployment team already there, and to prevent morale slippage in those yet to come. That was the task of communications.

Duval's view was this: "Men will work under poor conditions—of weather, transportation, housing, and everything else—if they have some idea what the hell is going on. One of the things you have to do more than ever, on a project such as this, is to feel the pulse of the employee out there on the job, and make sure he is given enough information as to where he stands and what is happening.

"In the factory, bang in and bang out, do the job and go home. But it means more away from home, out in the field, to keep him from thinking that nobody cares or knows what he is doing. And the most important medium of communication is in first-line supervision, the group leader, an assistant foreman out in the field."

Bill Duval knew the man he wanted to handle that vital link in getting the show going in England. With the dismal situation firmly in mind, he flew back to Florida to turn over command of the Douglas team there to Bill Stitt and tap his chosen man on the shoulder.

He was A. E. "Sarge" Willer, the craggy-faced Douglas veteran who had followed the Thor program from the early days, from Culver City and the DEI to the job of works supervisor at the Florida facilities.

Again, as it seemed so often in the high points and unhappy moments of the Thor program, it was just before Christmas that Duval asked Sarge to become his staff assistant in the United Kingdom. And it was the worst of times for Sarge to break the news to his wife, Darlene. For in the living room of their new home on Merritt Island, Mrs. Willer had just finished putting up the last of their new drapes.

Personnel, present and future, was a prime problem when Duval, Willer, and Clay Noah, already on the scene, gathered around a desk in Duval's headquarters office at RAF Feltwell in January, 1959, to tackle deployment in earnest. The force of some five hundred would rapidly have to be expanded to approximately one thousand. Until then the emphasis had been on bachelors whenever possible. Next in preference, in the first contingents through 1958, had been men with working wives, women who could do secretarial or clerical work, thus getting "double duty" from the obtainable living spaces. Last came those with small families, one or two children.

For the future, however, Duval insisted on highly capable, highly talented men, no matter if they had three children, or even four like himself. In point of fact, the factory had "run out" of the other types. The question of putting them up simply would have to be solved somehow; getting the skills was the important thing.

It was Noah who came up with a major part of the solution. Douglas had not received all the trailers. Most had gone to Feltwell, some to Hemswell in recent weeks, and others were being moved as the job demanded from Feltwell to

Hemswell. But the company still was authorized to purchase twenty-five more.

"Why not build those with 'pup' trailers behind them for the extra children?" Noah suggested.

"What?" Duval demanded. Noah had been doodling on a pad of paper. The rough sketch showed one of the typical caravans with a little one tagging along behind.

"Make everything dependent on the 'mother' caravan," he explained, "electricity and so on, with the connected little 'pup' trailer just a place for a couple of kids to sleep, with their wardrobes."

The trio put in an enthusiastic evening working up the idea. They sketched a small walkway between "mother" and "pup." There would be room for two bunks and a divan, which would open into a double bed. Heat would be from an electric heater, wired from the main caravan. By the next day wheels were turning to obtain bids from the Sprite Company, a trailer firm, for the unique housing expedient.

Allocation of the trailers already on hand or arriving also was a headache. Duval, however, concentrating first on morale factors as much as possible, worked out a military-style "point" system for priorities on living accommodations. It was based on the size of the family, with bachelors holding the least points. They received a break in return. Where two were put up together in a trailer, they were awarded the larger of the two versions being produced, which had separate bedrooms.

With operations rapidly moving away from the USAF facilities at Lakenheath, Duval also addressed himself to the recreation problem. Again it was in a semimilitary manner.

Joining with the top representatives of the other contractors, such as Rocketdyne, AC Spark Plug, and General Electric, a board of directors was formed of staff members from each for their own clubs at each squadron site. Duval presided at the meetings as "chairman," and got through to Leo Carter for an advance from Douglas to buy a jukebox and furniture, build the cocktail lounge, and stock the first club at RAF Hemswell. Local British managers were hired at each station to cater and manage the clubs.

They were not quite like Officers' Clubs fiscally. With the prospect of one operation phasing in while another still was phasing out, Duval noted that it was "something like moving a cocktail lounge from one part of Los Angeles to another every four months." But the dart games, adopted from the English pubs, other game facilities, Saturday night dance combos, banquet rooms for private parties and meeting rooms for the civilian team's "women's auxiliary," and occasional movies as well, proved a great shot in the arm for the general outlook during the gloomy months of snow and freezing fog that prevented travel to the cities.

The Air Force, unable to establish complete AFEX facilities due to the limited number of people, helped immeasurably by providing "delicatessen scale" AFEX facilities at each new Thor squadron site. The wives' morale was bettered when they were able to buy familiar brand names, even those who did most of their shopping in the nearby village or town. And they further found that the customary "two and six" per hour fee for baby sitters was a delightful markdown from what they had been paying in Florida or California.

The matter of communications had been put into Willer's hands by Duval as early as possible. From the start they recognized, in Willer's words, the "negative and neutral

thinking" after the foul weather of past months, the inadequate housing, and the slipping schedules. "There's a lot to
do," Duval told him. "Get out in the field and get with it."

It was a matter of turning the tide, and a rough job at the
start. Duval personally had his experiences with what they
later would term jokingly the "shock factor" of what so many
had faced initially on arrival, without adequate warning.

Through January, he had sought as desperately as anyone
else for quarters for his family, due in February. The only
thing he could nail down was a so-called "flat," a small group
of rooms knocked together by the Air Force Housing Office.
The address was fine: Brandon Park. That was one of the
formerly magnificent but long-disused country estates. But
the Duval part of the estate was in a damp-soaked tile-roofed
brick building that previously had been used as a work shed
or storage building. It had not been occupied as living quarters for fifty years.

It was there Duval came home the first night after his
family's arrival to find them huddled about the only real
source of heat, the coal-burning fireplace which took most
of the warmth up the chimney, to hear Char, with a slight
tremble in her voice, exclaim, "Oh, Bill! What have you
gotten us into?"

It was a far cry from sunny Florida or California. But once
the cry was over, they settled into their situation and spent
the next month drying out the walls with all the heat they
could muster from the coal-burner.

Like those walls, it was slow going to warm up the whole
program. But Duval, with the able help of Willer, Noah, and

the others of his staff, including his hard-working secretary Sally Wright, began stoking the boiler of new enthusiasm and activities. They perhaps could not see it themselves at the moment, but back at BMD headquarters in Southern California, Jamie Wallace noted to Colonel Jacobson what the latter already had sensed: "Things are shaping up."

Colonel Jake had good reason to know. He had spent eighty-nine days in England making sure they would.

26.

THE EAGLE'S EYE ...

Vandenberg AFB
February 28, 1959

THOR was to essay a historic new role this day.

For a full year, BMD and the contractors concerned had been working under highest national priority, assigned by the President, on WS-117L (Weapon System 117-L), known originally as Sentry. The goal was a reconnaissance satellite vehicle. As the program progressed, it was split into three parts: Discoverer, Midas, and Samos. All three versions would include an upper-stage rocket vehicle designed to go into orbit, built by Lockheed and called Agena. The satellite stage would be powered by a Bell Aircraft Company rocket engine burning the "hypergolic" combination of UDMH (unsymmetrical dimethyl hydrazine) and red fuming nitric acid. This highly volatile pairing is called hypergolic because the compounds burst into flame simply upon meeting, without ignition of any kind.

Midas was planned as an early-warning satellite. It would

226

have infrared sensors to detect the heat surge of the exhaust at the moment of an enemy ICBM's takeoff. Its name means "missile defense alarm system."

Samos's name for public consumption, declared meaningless at the time, was simply taken from a Greek island. It was, however, to be a camera-eyed satellite, ultimately taking over the chores of the top-secret ill-fated U-2 plane. And its name really stood for "satellite and missile observation system."

Discoverer, like Midas, was named more fittingly. It was to pioneer the way for Samos and Midas, and test out the concept and certain specialized components vital to the later success both of Midas and Samos.

All three were planned for polar orbits, circling the earth "vertically" while the earth turned "horizontally" within the satellite orbit, like a gyroscopic top. Thus every inch of the earth's surface eventually would pass under a polar satellite and whatever sensing devices or cameras it contained. Only a relatively small number of such satellites would be needed. They would complete a north-south-north orbit in some ninety minutes at approximately twenty-five thousand miles an hour. In that time, the earth would turn only 22½ degrees from west to east at nine hundred miles an hour.

The keen foresight of Air Force planners, recognizing the ultimate need for reconnaissance satellites while they still were struggling to get their first ballistic missile programs going, was a significant factor in the early 1956 selection of Camp Cooke for transformation into Vandenberg AFB. Just below Point Arguello, the California coast line turns sharply eastward. From there to the Straits of Magellan and Tierra del Fuego at the southernmost tip of South America, the coast line of the continents slants almost steadily eastward. That geographic fact makes this middle seaward jut of California the one suitable point in the continental United States where rockets can be fired due south without endangering populated communities or friendly neighbors by falling boosters or early "destructs." Nothing but the sea stretches between Vandenberg-Arguello and Antarctica.

The team to initiate the Discoverer series had been assembled months before, in the autumn of 1958. Colonel J. J. Cody headed the BMD field office. Lieutenant Colonel William R. Heisler was in charge of the military space programs, of which the Thor-boosted Discoverer would be the first, busiest, and most spectacular and successful for two years to come.

"Moose" Mathison, who once dashed out of the Cape Canaveral blockhouse to retrieve a fallen Thor fin, moved west to head the satellite tracking, control, and ultimately, re-entry-package recovery efforts.

And assigned to Vandenberg as the Discoverer chief of test operations was an unusual young man named Captain Rob Roy. A graduate of the United States Naval Academy with a degree in electrical engineering, he elected service with the Air Force, becoming thereby one of the select group of officers who have been missilemen throughout their careers, and started in the pre-BMD days. Rob Roy was assigned initially to Patrick AFB after a year's post-Annapolis study in electronics and guided missiles. He was launching control officer for nearly twoscore Matador guided missiles. He was LCO on thirty-seven launchings of the X-17 re-entry test vehicle that played such a vital role in confirming nose-cone theories vital to the ballistic missile program. And early in the Discoverer program, before the end of 1959, he was recognized as the man who had turned the key to send more successful earth satellites into orbit than any other man, in addition to controlling more peacetime missile launchings of all kinds than any other person.

Several attempts at launching Discoverer I had been scrubbed previously for reasons ranging from technical problems to the frequently foggy coastal weather.

The dawn on February 28, however, displayed a cloudless blue canopy from the far horizon of the Pacific Ocean on the west to the scrub-covered hills to the east. There would be no obstruction to necessary initial optical tracking and photography.

Inside the blockhouse all looked well also as the final 245-minute Discoverer countdown—much longer than a combat Thor alone, due to the complexity of the two-stage "bird" and its instrumentation—proceeded with extremely few "holds" for minor difficulties.

At 1:49 P.M., the Thor burst into life. With nothing less than stately grace, its elongated profile—measuring 78.2-feet with the Agena vehicle, 18.8 feet tall itself, wedded to the Thor's nose—speared upward.

For the first time in history, a ballistic rocket leaned almost due south, as its heat scratched a white mark of passage in the ice crystals of the chill upper levels of the air.

Almost at once, the Navy's Pacific Missile Range headquarters picked it up at Point Mugu, one hundred miles south. Minutes later, the Navy tracking ship, USNS Pvt. Joe E. Mann, stationed nearly one thousand miles below Vandenberg AFB, received signals. At Point Mugu the fifteen telemetric channels were coming in well. But the Pvt. Joe E. Mann said the beacon was "faint."

How faint? No one knew instantly. The radioed messages did not clarify the question. All anyone could do was wait, wait the full hour until the Thor-boosted Discoverer, weighing thirteen hundred pounds, passed over another of the special tracking stations.

That would be after the satellite should have crossed Antarctica near McMurdo Sound, tucked under the South Pole, then raced back up the night-side of earth, climbing over the Indian Ocean, tracing a path over Russia's Ural Mountains, and finally popping into earth's day-side again over the North Pole and down across Alaska.

A station was waiting on Kodiak Island, Alaska, to pick up the Discoverer's beacon signal. There was another station in Hawaii hoping to pick it up minutes after Alaska. But neither did.

Those were tense hours, probing, checking, calculating. Had Thor somehow failed? Had the upper stage failed?

The early tracking reports immediately after launching, picked up at Vandenberg and Point Mugu for six minutes, were fed through the computers. Everything indicated that both stages had performed as planned. Discoverer should be in orbit.

Rear Admiral John E. Clark, deputy director of the sponsoring Advance Research Projects Agency of DOD, put as much on record, in the scientist's version of those same words:

"It should be on orbit."

Guided by the deductions of the Air Force, Douglas, and Lockheed team, he further said the Cadillac-long satellite appeared "nearly right on" its planned course at the critical start. The admiral speculated that a nose cap, holding the beacon antennas in folded-down position, might not have sprung free, thus muffling its voice over the Navy range ship and choking if off entirely over the Alaska and Hawaii stations where it would be farther from the receivers.

There was nothing to do but wait, with Colonel Cody doing the most difficult part of the waiting. He sat with a telephone to his ear for hours. Then finally the word came. The radio definitely was out. But based on calculations from the original tracking, radar had picked it up.

Blasted to space by Thor, Discoverer I was in orbit.

It was not the perfect orbit they had sought, nor the orbit "more perfectly round than the earth itself" which another Discoverer would achieve later. But Thor had sent up a vehicle of more than half a ton, one that could then fire itself into the aerospace age's first north-south-north polar orbit.

Moreover, it had aboard an infrared "horizon scanner," an ingenious device to sense the heat difference between the curving earth's edge ahead and the chill of space, then cause hydrogen peroxide jets to adjust its course in response.

More than a year before the U-2 and its pilot, Francis Powers, went down in Russia, their replacement was on the way.

Thanks to Thor's mighty, ever more reliable boost, a new eye was being developed in space that could ignore the Iron Curtain. Its first vision was dim, barely able to see the horizon. But it would get better. It would become the eye of an eagle—the American eagle.

27.

...AND THE LION'S ROAR

Vandenberg AFB
April 12 to 16, 1959

LEADING journalists from Great Britain had reached Vandenberg AFB April 12 on a tour of American missile facilities and factories arranged by the USAF. Emphasis naturally was on Thor, to erase remaining doubts in the United Kingdom—whether politically or privately held—as to its capability and reliability. Already the visitors had been briefed at the Pentagon by Air Force Secretary Douglas and General Curtis LeMay, whisked to Milwaukee for a visit to the AC Spark Plug guidance component plant, shown the static test firing of a Thor engine at Rocketdyne's facilities in the Santa Susana Mountains near Los Angeles, and taken through the production line at Douglas in Santa Monica. Already one of the most widely respected writers of the group, Chapman Pincher, had cabled a dispatch to his paper, the *London Daily Express,* declaring that the trip had "put the suspect Thor in an entirely different light. Far from being 'just junk,' as the Socialists have claimed, I can testify that Thor is now a highly reliable weapon."

Even more impressive evidence was in store. On the morning of April 13, the reporters attended the regular prelaunching briefing for the American press, then joined the motorcade from First Missile Division headquarters to the observation site near the beach. This was the day Discoverer II was to be launched.

Weather, technical problems, and certain new aspects of this second Discoverer combined ideally to create a proper mood of heightening suspense for the visitors. The typical coastal morning fog almost obscured the white pencil of the Thor-Agena poking above the sand dunes at seaside.

Lieutenant Colonel James Marquis, manning the microphone on the communications truck parked by the bleachers and the working-press benches, reported the countdown status and the necessary holds until the sun burned away the fog. Shortly after 11 A.M. they were treated to Vandenberg's own peculiar delay, a northbound train, shepherded through by a helicopter.

Just before 1 P.M., the pace suddenly quickened at T minus eleven minutes. There was just a brief planned hold at T minus 2½ minutes, for a final check. Suddenly it was "zero." The first surge of flame from the Rocketdyne engine blasted up enough sand to make the cloud briefly yellow. Then the rocket combination emerged, climbing. Thor 170 was performing beautifully, filling the Santa Ynez Valley with its throaty roar, pushing the satellite vehicle upward and finally out of sight to the south. But this did not end the suspense either for the British or the Americans.

At the briefing, William H. Godel, planning director for

ARPA, had disclosed two exciting points. While no life was aboard, Discoverer II contained an "environmental capsule" equipped to measure an oxygen supply and temperatures within itself. It was the forerunner of a "life support" capsule, first for mice, later for monkeys. And there was just a "one thousand to one" chance that the capsule would be recovered. The eight C-119 "flying boxcars" of the USAF's 6593rd Test Squadron were alert at Hickman AFB, Hawaii, for the first attempt to "snatch" in midair a recovery package to be ejected from the satellite the following day. That was to be on its seventeenth orbit of the earth. The signal to eject would be sent up on the sixteenth orbital pass from Kodiak Island, Alaska. Timing was such, if all went well, that the 195-pound package would arc downward into the atmosphere, slowed by a retrorocket. At a specified altitude above the sea, a pressure-sensing device would pop open an orange-and-white-checkered parachute over a recovery "ball park," fifty miles wide and two hundred miles long, southwest of Hawaii. Then, as the package emitted a radio beacon signal, the C-119 "boxcars" would home on it and attempt to snag the descending chute with special harnesses trailing from their open-end cargo compartments.

Two hours after the launching, Discoverer II was declared in satisfactory orbit and reporting in "loud and clear." British and Americans alike retired to the taproom of the Santa Maria Inn to speculate on the next day's double promise.

Not only was there the slim chance of the first recovery on record of a package from a satellite, but the RAF men in training at Vandenberg were scheduled to launch their first Thor.

April 14, however, brought bad news on both projects.

The timing mechanism of Discoverer II proved faulty. It ejected the re-entry pack too soon, over the icy wastes north of Spitzbergen, Norway. That much was known from visual sightings and telemetric data. Aerial search was instituted, but neither the capsule nor the colorful checkerboard parachute was found.

As for Thor 161, the first to bear the red, white, and blue *rondel* of the RAF, it could have been launched under wartime necessity. But the understandable caution with which such an initial firing was approached in peacetime led to several technical delays. By the time they were checked out, the weather had closed in and the event was scrubbed for the day.

It was the same story the next day. A minor problem in the guidance component, then the weather again delayed the shot.

The smell of success was in the air, though, when the crew gathered on April 16, determined to mark out a milestone in British military history. The VIP observers from the United Kingdom felt it. They included Air Vice-Marshal W. Sheen and Air Vice-Marshal G. A. (Gus) Walker.

Group Captain R. T. Frogley, senior RAF officer at Vandenberg in charge of trainees who later would command the fifteen-Thor squadron headquartered at Driffield, felt assured. And confidence exuded from the RAF launching crew, whose backgrounds so thoroughly embraced all constituencies of Great Britain that they could not have been chosen with better representation.

Heading the team as LCO was Squadron Leader Peter G.

Coulson, born at Cardiff, South Wales, at thirty-seven years of age already in his twenty-first year of active duty with the RAF. His wife and three children were then living at Fairview, Cardiff, awaiting his return from the United States. Squadron Leader Coulson had taken his pilot training and flying instructor course as long ago as 1942–43 in Southern Rhodesia. He commanded a transport squadron just prior to his assignment to Thor in 1958.

Squadron Leader Coulson's missile maintenance technician linked the crew to two far-opposite ends of the home island. He was Chief Technician Roy M. Carpenter, thirty-five years old. While born at Dover on the English Channel, his wife and two sons were waiting at her home town, as impressive in name as the spread of Chief Technician Carpenter's mustache; her home was Jackston of Melrose, Gamrie, by Banff, Banffshire, Scotland.

The third member of the crew, fittingly, was English in all aspects, born at Croydon in Surrey, and still calling home no farther away than East Croydon, where his Yorkshire wife and two children awaited his return. This was Master Pilot Maurice H. Sloan, thirty-five, with over nineteen years' active duty and now assigned as launching monitor console operator.

(An "alternate crew" assigned to the first RAF launching was composed of Flight Lieutenant Harold E. V. Ford, twenty-nine years old, born at Lonrorla, India, launching control officer; Master Pilot John Anderson, thirty-five, a native of Moravshire, Scotland, launching monitor console officer; and Chief Technician Frederick A. E. Chivers, thirty-six, missile maintenance technician, who hailed originally from Penge, in Kent.)

When the order came to launch, in the early afternoon, Chief Technician Carpenter's work was done. All settings and adjustments were ready. At T minus fifteen minutes, his job was to stand by in the blockhouse to repair any malfunction, either in GSE or the missile itself, that might develop.

But none did. Master Pilot Sloan, watching the phase sequencing and the thirty malfunction indicators on the launching monitor console, found no reason to impose any technical holds.

At T minus fourteen minutes the protective shed rolled away. The first RAF Thor came erect on the training pad at the command of Squadron Leader Coulson, given by the turn of a key. Fueling began. Soon the thick waist of Thor was wreathed in frosty vapors. The only delay was a planned one, at T minus four. The range safety officer took a last look and declared the range clear.

The brief remaining countdown was resumed. At 12:46 P.M. the now familiar surge of "fire in the tail" leaped into life, and the wave of sound rolled two miles across the beach lands to break upon the observers' ears. VIPs, press, and 280 RAF trainees joined in the cheers as the button-nosed ballistic missile pushed up through a cloud fragment, broke into the blue again and headed over the Pacific for its 1,500-mile journey.

"The Lion's Roar," as the code name dubbed the launching, was entirely successful, true to the target area at ten thousand miles an hour. Group Captain Frogley declared that Thor had now "taken its place in the RAF armory." General Wade expressed his personal congratulations to the British. And Squadron Leader Coulson pocketed the launching key as a personal souvenir.

The flush of the day's triumph was topped with the playing of "God Save the Queen" via a recording thoughtfully borrowed in advance from a Santa Maria radio station.

And when the RAF graduates took leave of Vandenberg AFB, they left behind a memento of the historic day. It was a wall plaque for the office of the resident RAF liaison officer. Lettered in Old English, it said:

It came to pass that on the day set aside for the firing, the mighty god Thor lay stricken of guidance.

And in the camp of SAC and amongst the tribe of Douglas, the followers didst turn around in circles.

And amongst them were those who rotated violently. They were known as wheels!

The Army of the RAF didst give succor to Thor and administer unto him wine and victuals.

And Thor was pleased, and didst issue much vapor, and utter a mighty roar, and ascend into the heavens and roar his praises to the multitude below.

28.

EMILY—LOOKING BRIGHTER

England
May 1 to December 31, 1959

As FAR as the weather was concerned, it was to be what one of Bill Duval's British friends termed "the nicest summer in two hundred years." The Douglas deployment chief could not vouch for that, but with springtime breaking in May, it did seem that the sun was shining on Project Emily. In the words of Sarge Willer, "the tide had been turned." Morale was bounding upward. Work was progressing faster, even though there was a great deal more of it, and the Douglas "Little America" colony was spread in varying degrees over all four squadrons.

The installation and checkout phase was virtually complete at the RAF Feltwell complex. The last brick-and-mortar work was finished at RAF Hemswell on April 30, and the biggest contracting effort to instrument and activate the launchers now was centered there. Basic steel-and-concrete work had been under way since last December 22 at RAF

239

Driffield, the third fifteen-missile complex, and was near the halfway mark. And ground had been broken at the fourth and final squadron, RAF North Luffenham, on April 16.

Project Emily was moving back on schedule, and many factors, beyond the communications lines Sarge Willer set up between Duval and the teams in the field, could be credited.

Most of the solutions that Bill Duval implemented, beginning with the second squadron at Hemswell, were mothered by necessity. On transfer northward from Feltwell, the Douglas "gypsies" were out of reach of the USAF facilities—the American schools, doctors, and clubs, for instance—that they had enjoyed at Lakenheath AFB.

To solve the medical problem, he had two of the bigger trailers built into complete medical facilities. One went immediately to Hemswell, the other to Driffield, with the first to leapfrog to the final site at North Luffenham when the need grew bigger there. Each was staffed with Douglas nurses flown over from California. At each site, local doctors were contracted to hold office hours daily in the trailers. When Douglasites saw the English doctors in the trailers, they paid only the nominal British office call fee. The doctors, however, also made house calls to the individual family caravans as needed.

Realizing that he had to provide all the services of a "city," Duval employed a British organization called the Secure Corporation, similar to American privately-contracted plant protection officers, to police the caravan communities. They attended to everything from traffic control and infrequent complaints about a "noisy party in the neighborhood" to keeping a friendly eye out for the children at play.

Education was another problem. English schools nearby quite often were as overcrowded as their counterparts back in the United States.

Here each family had to reach its own solution. Some sent their children to the village day schools. Others made use of the Air Force boarding schools in London. Still others, such as Duval and Willer, arranged for tuition at English boarding schools. The Duvals sent their two older boys, Bill, Junior, fifteen, and Quinton, eleven, to Gresham's School in Holt, near Norwich in Norfolk. Both boys got on famously, especially in sports, even though it took awhile to understand kippers for breakfast. Char was properly proud of young Bill when he made the house Rugger team, and Bill senior pretended that he was not the least bit surprised when both boys excelled at swimming. "They don't have much chance at it here," he figured. "About one month a year and that's it. They put up swimming, like they do their cars, for the winter. Just not enough training."

The "Emily Clubs" at RAF Hemswell and later at Driffield and North Luffenham proved their worth quickly. And as the evening daylight lengthened—in midsummer it is light until 10:30 P.M. in the northern latitudes—many sports events were added. Softball teams were formed. A driving range was set up at one base. Nine-hole golf tournaments could be played after dinner.

With schedules becoming something less than daylight-to-dusk grinds, increasing numbers developed the foreign-car bug. The tendency to adopt British slang—going to the village store was going to the "bloke store"—was even extended in this respect. Where British cars were "bloke-mobiles," French vehicles became "frogmobiles" and German autos "krautmobiles."

In the matter of housing, the full complement of trailers now was on hand. When the last of this group pulled up stakes at Feltwell, they were careful to take along their "Los Angeles City Limits" sign. At Driffield they chose a new title, "Santa Monica on the Wolds," in reference to the Midlands' chalk rock outcroppings. At one time, Duval's domain included the world's largest single trailer park. For the caravanless bachelors, arrangements were made with the RAF to lease barracks at the disused airfields. Douglas then furnished them and contracted locally for "batman" service.

In short, DAC meant two things in England in 1959. One was Douglas Aircraft Company; the other, Direct Action Committee. The latter "ban the bomb" group did not halt its propaganda activities for unilateral disarmament by Great Britain as an example to the world, with the Thor bases as one of its specific targets of complaint. But the demonstrations now were aimed more at Trafalgar Square in London, and the Douglas people, moving gradually northward, deeper into the country, found themselves enjoying increasingly cordial relationships with the local people.

Wives soon discovered the wonders of the antique shops, for instance, and the antique dealers as rapidly discovered the wives.

In the more technical sense, program progress and personal relationships went hand in hand. The supply system for construction and resupply system for the increasing number